CRITICAL ACCLAIM

If all species were somehow protected in perpetuity as just single viable populations, there would be no further decline in *species* biodiversity. But we would all die, because many populations of many species are necessary to supply the ecosystem services that support humanity. One of the great problems of conservation is thus the conservation of *populations*, and a critical tool for doing that is baseline information that can be used to determine how population diversity is changing. Napa County's Breeding Birds is a wonderful example of what is needed; it should serve as a model for breeding bird atlases for every county in the U.S.A.

> Paul R. Ehrlich, author, *The Birder's Handbook, The Population Bomb*

This document is the only accurate and thoroughly researched thesis on the nesting avifauna in Napa County. It reflects the results of a five-year field survey by a core of 74 field ornithologists of the Napa-Solano Audubon Society. This atlas should stand in the library of and should often be consulted by all government and management agencies and, of course, will become a reference companion to all naturalists, biologists and birders in Northern California.

> Rich Stallcup, Naturalist, PRBO Conservation Science

This well-designed and well-done Breeding Bird Atlas will serve as a basis against which future bird populations in Napa County can be compared. All persons interested in Napa County birds or Napa County land use policies will want to have this authoritative work at hand for reference.

> Benjamin D. Parmeter, author, *Birds of Sonoma County, California*

Lavishly illustrated, the Napa Breeding Bird Atlas provides vital information on the current status, distribution, habitat needs, timing of occurrence, and changes in historic status of all the county's nesting birds. The atlas is an essential book for anyone seeking to understand the intricate lifestyles of local birds, the ebb and flow of avian cycles, and which species need conservation actions to protect their habitats from threats posed by humans.

> David Shuford, author, *The Marin County Breeding Bird Atlas*

As bird populations shift and change, too often declining, studies like the Napa County breeding bird atlas provide an essential inventory of the breeding birds of the region. This book shows the diversity and the richness of Napa County and should be a standard reference for birders, conservationists, and land-use planners in the county.

> David Allen Sibley, author, *The Sibley Guide to Birds*

D1617336

(Foldout Map)

Napa County Highways, Cities and Waterways

BREEDING BIRDS
OF
NAPA COUNTY,
CALIFORNIA

Major funding for publication provided by a grant from the
Giles W. and Elise G. Mead Foundation

Breeding Birds
of Napa County, California

An illustrated atlas of nesting birds

Authors
Murray Berner
Bill Grummer
Robin Leong
Mike Rippey

Editor
Ann Smith

Cover Illustration
Lazuli Bunting
Sophie Webb

Cover Design
Kathleen Tandy

NAPA-SOLANO AUDUBON SOCIETY

Copyright @ 2003 by Napa-Solano Audubon Society

All rights reserved. This book may not be reproduced, in whole
or in part, including illustrations, in any form without written
permission from the publishers, except by a reviewer for the
public press who wishes to quote brief passages.

Library of Congress Cataloging-in-Publication Data:
Authors: Berner, Murray, 1955- ; Grummer, Bill, 1940- ;
Leong, Robin, 1943- ; Rippey, Mike 1949-
Editor: Smith, Ann, 1932-
Breeding birds of Napa County, California: an illustrated atlas
of nesting birds
p. 204   28 cm.
Includes bibliographic references and index (9 p.)
1. Birds – California – Napa County.   2. Bird populations –
California – Napa County – Geographical distribution.   3.
Napa County (California) – Natural history.   I. Title.
QL684.C2.B47   2003   598'.09794'19
2002115834

ISBN 0-615-12290-6

Library of Congress control number: 2002115834

Printed in the United States of America, using soy-based inks
and recycled paper, by Alonzo Printing Company, Inc., Hayward, California, certified as a Green Business by the Alameda
County Green Business Program.

Published 2003 by:
Napa-Solano Audubon Society
P. O. Box 5027
Vallejo, CA 94591

CONTENTS

American Avocets

A place and time of rest and reflection,
a birder's metaphor.

PREFACE

The Napa-Solano Audubon Society enthusiastically embraced the nationwide concept of breeding bird atlases in the late 1980s, and a dedicated and able committee consisting of Marguerite (Peggy) Gross, Bill Grummer, Marjorie Irwin, Robin Leong, and Mike Rippey set off on the task of producing an atlas for Napa County. They recruited the extensive network of volunteers, produced the materials necessary to document the research, sorted and preserved the resultant data, and provided the impetus for this volume. The general fieldwork took place over five years, ending in 1993.

Napa County is famous for its vineyards and wines. In order to preserve agriculture and prevent development, the county passed a landmark ordinance in 1968, with rural areas protected from subdivisions and dedicated to farming. As the wine industry prospered, agriculture in the county changed from a varied pattern of orchards, truck farms, Christmas tree farms, grazing lands, and some vineyards into nearly a monoculture of vineyards. Napa's flora and fauna changed accordingly, and the breeding bird atlas study took place near the climax of that habitat alteration.

The county contains the long, fertile Napa Valley between mountain ranges on the east and west, with marshes on the south where it touches San Pablo Bay. It has two large lakes, a few large parks, and some smaller parks and reserves. The Napa River traverses the valley, and its many creeks flow down the mountains. That rich environment produced a total of 156 breeding bird species found during the atlas study, of which 145 were confirmed and 11 others were considered probable or possible breeding birds.

Clearly, no study can touch every inch of available habitat. However, established scientific parameters were observed throughout the fieldwork. The resultant data creates a cornerstone upon which current studies may determine which bird species are threatened by human activities and future studies may uncover changes in the distribution of birds in Napa County, in the hope that our avifauna can be protected.

The goal of every participant who waded through poison oak, crunched the numbers, worried about the weather, listened for the song of breeding birds, and in any way contributed to this volume is to help ensure the survival of birds, animals, and native plants in an environment that supports the human race.

—Ann Smith, Editor

ACKNOWLEDGMENTS

Sponsor: Napa-Solano Audubon Society

Breeding Bird Atlas Steering Committee (1988): Marguerite (Peggy) Gross, Bill Grummer, Marjorie Irwin, Robin Leong, and Mike Rippey

Area Coordinators: North, Bill Grummer; South, Mike Rippey; Roving, Robin Leong

Computer Committee: Phil Burton, Chair; Ann Lincoln, Bill Grummer

Newsletter: Marguerite Gross, Editor; Bill Grummer, Robin Leong, Mike Rippey

Ad Hoc Breeding Bird Atlas Committee (2002): Ann Smith, Chair; Janet Barth, Margaret Barson, Keith Gish, Bill Grummer, Jim Hench, Marge Irwin, Jerry Karr, Robin Leong, Jo Maillard, Mike Rippey, David Takeuchi, Kathleen Tandy, Louise Vicencio, Alan Wight

Distribution Maps: Alan Wight

Other Maps: Janet Barth, Margaret Barson, Jim Hench

Desktop Publishing: Keith Gish

Cover Design: Kathleen Tandy

Species Accounts Text: Murray Berner

Technical Review: Murray Berner, Bill Grummer, Robin Leong, Mike Rippey

Editorial and Production Assistance: Joan Ferguson, Marguerite Gross, Ellen Sabine, Fran Scarlett, Uzelle Williams

References: Jo Maillard

Art Committee: David Takeuchi, Chair; Joanne Castro, Joan Ferguson, Fran Scarlett, Keith Gish

Illustrators: **Linda Adams** (American Goldfinch, Black-necked Stilt, Blue-gray Gnatcatcher, Cinnamon Teal, Northern Mockingbird, Northern Pintail, Oak Titmouse, Ruddy Duck, Spotted Sandpiper, Virginia Rail, Western Bluebird, White-breasted Nuthatch, Yellow Warbler); **Shawneen Finnegan** (Acorn Woodpecker, American Avocet, American Robin, Ash-throated Flycatcher, Barn Swallow, Black-headed Grosbeak, Canvasback, Clark's Grebe, Dark-eyed Junco, Lesser Goldfinch, Lesser Scaup, Northern Shoveler, Osprey, Purple Martin, Pygmy Nuthatch, Savannah Sparrow, Snowy Plover, Song Sparrow, Violet-green Swallow, Western Scrub-Jay, Yellow-headed Blackbird, Yellow-rumped Warbler); **Dana Gardner** (Clapper Rail, Hooded Oriole, House Sparrow, Red-winged Blackbird, Rock Dove, Spotted Towhee, Yellow-billed Magpie); **David Haupt** (Chipping Sparrow, Orange-crowned Warbler, Warbling Vireo, Western Wood-Pewee, Yellow-breasted Chat); **Keith Hansen** (Barn Owl, California Thrasher, Common Poorwill, Greater Roadrunner, Horned Lark, Mountain Quail, White-tailed Kite, White-throated Swift); **Zev Labinger** (American Kestrel, Bald Eagle, Belted Kingfisher, Brown Creeper, Burrowing Owl, Cooper's Hawk, Golden Eagle, Killdeer, Northern Harrier, Peregrine Falcon, Prairie Falcon, Red-shouldered Hawk, Red-tailed Hawk, Sharp-shinned Hawk, Steller's Jay, Turkey Vulture); **Rochelle Mason** (American Coot, American Crow, Brewer's Blackbird, Canada Goose, Cliff Swallow, Common Moorhen, Common Raven, Double-crested Cormorant, Great Egret, Great Horned Owl, House Finch, Long-eared Owl, Mallard, Mourning Dove, Northern Pygmy-Owl, Northern Saw-whet Owl); **Edward Rooks** (Brown-headed Cowbird, California Towhee, Mandarin Duck, Northern Rough-winged Swallow, Purple Finch, Western Meadowlark, Wild Turkey); **Lydia C. Thompson** (Blue-winged Teal, Phainopepla, Short-eared Owl); **Sophie Webb** (Allen's Hummingbird, American Dipper, Anna's Hummingbird, Band-tailed Pigeon, Bewick's Wren, Black Phoebe, Black Rail, Black-chinned Hummingbird, Black-crowned Night-Heron, Black-throated Gray Warbler, Bullock's Oriole, California Quail, Canyon Wren, Caspian Tern, Cassin's Vireo, Cedar Waxwing, Chestnut-backed Chickadee, Bushtit, Common Merganser, Common Yellowthroat, Downy Woodpecker, Dusky Flycatcher, European Starling, Forster's Tern, Gadwall, Grasshopper Sparrow, Great Blue Heron, Green Heron, Hairy Woodpecker, Hermit Thrush, House Wren, Hutton's Vireo, Lark Sparrow, Lawrence's Goldfinch, Lazuli Bunting, Loggerhead Shrike, MacGillivray's Warbler, Marsh Wren, Northern Flicker, Nuttall's Woodpecker, Olive-sided Flycatcher, Pacific-slope Flycatcher, Pied-billed Grebe, Pileated Woodpecker, Pine Siskin, Red-breasted Nuthatch, Ring-necked Pheasant, Rock Wren, Rufous-crowned Sparrow, Sage Sparrow, Snowy Egret, Sora, Spotted Owl, Swainson's Thrush, Tree Swallow, Tricolored Blackbird, Western Grebe, Western Kingbird, Western Screech-Owl, Western Tanager, Wilson's Warbler, Winter Wren, Wood Duck, Wrentit)

Major Funding: Anonymous (2), In memory of John Applegarth, Bob Barnes, Margaret Barson, Art and Aliece Battiste, Nicholas and Dominique-Smith Battiste, Stephanie Battiste, Tom and Jane Blaisdell, John Boyd, Robert Brittan, Joanne Castro, Christian Brothers Justin Community, Eleanor Dommerich, Richard Epstein, Dick and Carol Eyheralde, Joan Ferguson, John Galloway, George Gamble, Keith and Phyllis Gish, In memory of Marguerite Gross, Pat and Tom Hildreth, Bruce and Marjorie Irwin, Jerry and Theresa Karr, Charlotte Kisling, Cecilia Lee, Dr. William and Carlee Leftwich, Robin Leong, Jo Maillard, Marin Audubon Society, In memory of Dorothy Marsden, Robert Martin, Peter and Carlene Mennen, Mount Diablo Audubon Society, Napa County Wildlife Conservation Commission, Napa-Solano Audubon Society, John O'Connell, Richard and Doris Panzer, Myrlee Potosnak, William and Doris Proctor, William Provan, Dr. Alan Ringard,

ACKNOWLEDGMENTS

Dorothy Salvato, Phil and Dee Dee Sary, Fran Scarlett, Judith Sears, Sam Shummon, Duane and Ann Smith, Dean and Pat Stahr, In memory of Ted Stiewig, Frank Stout, David Takeuchi, Peter Whyte, Ted and Rochella Wooster. *Significant funding was secured through a Birdathon and Silent Auction conducted by Tony Battiste, and a major grant from the Giles W. and Elise G. Mead Foundation.*

Cooperating Agencies: Audubon Canyon Ranch (Heron and Egret Project), California Department of Fish and Game, California State Parks Department, Friends of the Napa River, Napa County Bird Rescue Center, PRBO Conservation Science, San Francisco State University, United States Fish and Wildlife Service, United States Bureau of Reclamation, United States Bureau of Land Management

Participants: Linda Adams, Lee and Andy Angel, John Arnold, Dick Ashford, Rich Bertoli, Nicholas Biehle, Phil Burton, Betty Burridge, Chuck Carpy, Joanne Castro, Glenn Clifton, Harold Connor, Chris and Wendy Cole, Rollo Darby, Fran Demgen, Miles Eisenman, George Finger, Bob and Carol Foley, George Gamble, Keith Gish, Marguerite Gross, Bill Grummer, Jean Hardin, Alta Hodgkins, Ted Hiatt, Ralph and Evelyn Ingols, Marjorie and Bruce Irwin, Tim Jenkins, Henry Junemann, Guy Kay, Jerry Karr, Jim Knight, Dolora Koontz, Lucinda LaMaster, Robin Leong, Jo Maillard, Billie Mangold, Herb McGrew, June Morgan, John O'Connell, Sue Overstreet, Mike & Sally Parmeter, John Parmeter, Marjorie Plant, Bob and Bertha Rains, Marian and Jack Rands, Karen Rippey, Mike Rippey, Arnold Roessler, Ruth Rudesill, Jake Ruygt, Ellen Sabine, Fran Scarlett, Sam Shummon, Duane and Ann Smith, Vic Snider, David Takeuchi, Edith Taylor, Wayne Tillay, Bruce Wallace, Alan Wight, Jon Winter, Chris Wood, Ted Wooster

Others Contributing Data: Alex Aragon, Audubon Canyon Ranch (John Kelly), Avocet Research Associates (Jules Evens), Yvonne Barker, Bob Bennett, Connie Bogosian, Terry Chappell, George Clark, Jay Cook, Ralph Deuer, Peggy Dickson, Cora Disney, Marne Donaldson, Jack Ellis, Jim Frediani, Sandy Frediani, Sharyn Fernandez, Don Griffin, Carole Grummer, Forrest Grummer, Jared Grummer, Thelma Halterman, Wallace Hardin, Marion Hildebrandt, Randy Hodge, Alta Hodgkins, Elgie Kirkpatrick, Monte Kirven, Zev Labinger, Norman Livermore, Chris Madrigal, Shar Maglione, Cary Manette, Bob Martinez, Frank Mauer, Stu and Gretchen McIndoe, Parry Mead, Linda Moran, Bryan Munn, Naomi Niermeyer, Terry Nordbye, Connie O'Shea, Craig Philpott, Myrlee Potosnak, Ruth Pratt, Mark Purdy, Bob Renati, Linda Richel, Santa Cruz Predatory Research Group (Brian Walton), Chuck Saunders, Gail Sharpsteen, David Shuford, Dara Skuce, Mark Sogge, Peter Sorensen, Martha Spence, Bonnie Stanislawski, Randy Sternberg, Sandy Stillwell, George Stratton, Thelma Stratton, Lorrie Thomas, Vince Tofanelli, Arnold Tudal, Larry Vermeulen, Al Vosher, Wes Weeks, Carl Wilcox, Wildlife Rescue Center of Napa County, Lynn Winter, Rosalie Woods, and Ralph Wright

Special Thanks

A breeding bird atlas is only possible with the help of many individuals, organizations, and landowners. The Napa County Breeding Bird Atlas was no exception. We wish to thank Doug Ellis for providing us with tapes of owls and Professor Don Hemphill of Pacific Union College for giving us some idea of what historically bred in Napa County. William G. Bousman gave us valued access to his unpublished compilation of Bay Area breeding records. Assistance came from Lloyd Kiff, curator of the Western Foundation of Vertebrate Zoology, and from Stephen Bailey, the collections Manager at the University of California, Berkeley Museum of Vertebrate Zoology, and later at the California Academy of Sciences. Donald Stoner, son of Emerson Stoner, provided his father's egging notes and notebooks. Thanks go to Dee Warenycia from the California Department of Fish and Game's Natural Diversity Data Base and to Jim Swanson, supervising biologist, Dennis Becker, biologist, and Blair Hayman, scientific aide, with the California Department of Fish and Game, Yountville. Our deep appreciation for generously sharing their experience goes to Betty Burridge of the Sonoma County Breeding Bird Atlas, Don Roberson of the Monterey County Breeding Bird Atlas, and David Shuford of the Marin County Breeding Bird Atlas. Napa County gave us valuable aid, particularly Jeff Tangen of the Conservation Division.

And of course, a big thank you to large and small property owners who allowed us to enter habitat that probably had never before been censused for birds. Those were: Aetna Springs Golf Course (Ket Stuth), John Ahmann, John Basset, Bureau of Reclamation (Arnold Roessler), California Department of Fish and Game (Jim Swanson), Calistoga Public Works, Cargill Salt (formerly Leslie Salt) (Chuck Taylor), Mary Casanova, Orlando and Maureen Chavez, Cleary Property (California State University Hayward), Joe Erasmy, Flying L Ranch (Paul Tipton), George Gamble, Mary Ann Gamble, Herbert Gunn, Wallace and Jean Hardin, Warren Kubler, Land Trust of Napa County (John Hoffnagle), George, John, Norman, Putnam, and Robert Livermore, Bob Long, David Long, Bob Martinez, Frank Mauer, Giles Mead, Napa County Airport (Leonard Peterson), Napa City Planning Department, Napa City Water Division, Napa Sanitation District (Ernie Erskine, Bill Gaffney, Clark Roach), Oakville Ranch (Wayne Ryan), Norman Pease, Noelle Peterson, Mark Purdy, R-Ranch at the Lake (Ruth Parker), Grace St. Amand, St. Helena Sanitation and Water District, Norman Solari, John Sutro, Vallejo Public Works Department (Ex Ganding, Jr., Water Superintendent, and Karl Voigt), Wild Horse Creek (Steve Hale), White Sulphur Springs (Betty and Buzz Foote).

—Robin Leong

NAPA'S BREEDING BIRDS
text by
Murray Berner

American Kestrel

Special Note:
 All historical records cited but not otherwise credited in the species accounts came from unpublished records of either Murray Berner or Bill Grummer.

SPECIES ACCOUNT DIRECTORY

All confirmed to breed in Napa County except six birds noted "probable" (Blue-winged Teal, Common Merganser, Northern Saw-whet Owl, Dusky Flycatcher, Phainopepla, and Yellow-rumped Warbler) and five noted "possible" (Sora, Burrowing Owl, Short-eared Owl, Black-chinned Hummingbird and MacGillivray's Warbler). Species listed in taxonomic order.

16

SPECIES ACCOUNT DIRECTORY

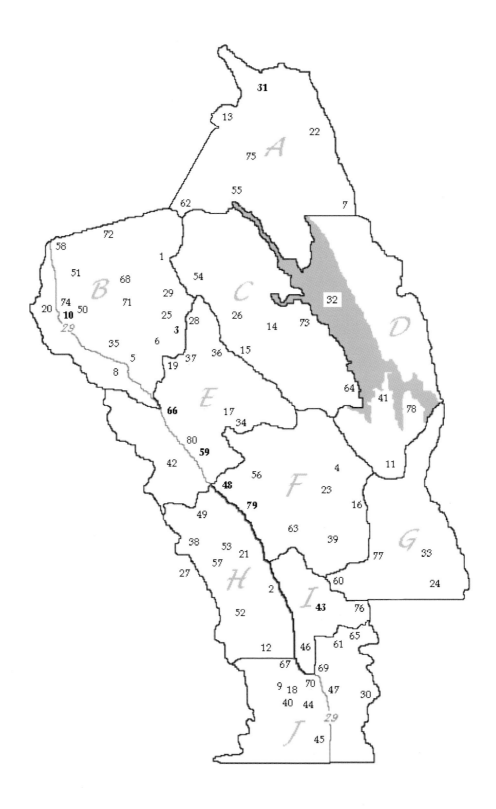

NAPA COUNTY NAMES

City names in **bold type**

SWEBB

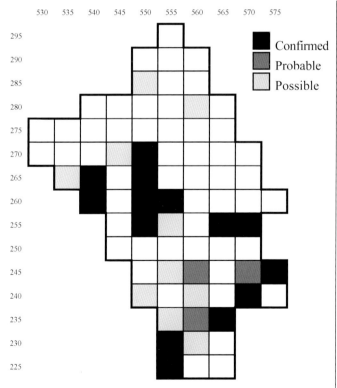

Year-round resident
Earliest confirmation May 6 – Nest building
Latest confirmation July 28 – Recently fledged young

The Pied-billed Grebe is a common winter resident of fresh-water reservoirs and of brackish water in the tidal district. Resident pairs remain to nest at many of the fresh-water sites, but summering grebes are rare on salt water. Nesting grebes require lakes and ponds larger than 0.5 acre in size, greater than 10 inches deep, with dense stands of submerged or emergent vegetation to which they anchor a floating nest (Muller and Storer 1999). Human-created wetlands, primarily small ranch ponds and irrigation reservoirs, satisfy these needs in Napa County.

Most Atlas confirmations involve precocial young and flightless fledglings. A May 5 mid-Napa Valley nest building record and a nest with young in Wild Horse Valley on June 5 are the exceptions. Exclusive of a July 28 Lake Hennessey report, observations of young span May 17-July 1. The remainder of the data extended more than three months from March 15. Each of the 17 blocks reporting abundance estimated ten or fewer pairs.

Pied-billeds were found on small ponds and reservoirs in eighteen of the 27 reporting priority blocks, primarily in the Pope, Wooden, Capell, and Napa Valleys. Grebes perhaps nested on salt water in the southwestern-most block. Six records, including at least three confirmed, came from Lake Hennessey, Lake Curry, and Lake Berryessa. Grebes apparently do not nest at Berryessa, perhaps due to inadequate shoreline vegetation or human disturbance. The seemingly insignificant smallest reservoirs support most of the county's nesting population.

Sponsored by Richard and Doris Panzer

WESTERN GREBE
Aechmophorus occidentalis

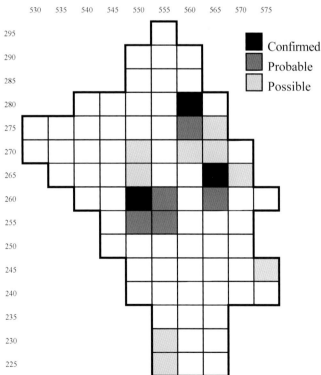

Confirmed
Probable
Possible

Resident year-round, more numerous in winter
Earliest confirmation June 17 - Precocial young
Latest confirmation October 22 - Carrying food

It is likely that Napa's breeding Western Grebes are year-round residents. They prefer large lakes, and hundreds winter on Hennessey and Berryessa, where a few remain to breed. In addition to large lake size, grebes require extensive emergent shoreline vegetation in which to place their nests (Storer and Nuechterlein 1992).

At the mouth of Eticuera Creek, a long-time resident observed precocial young on June 17, 1991, the observer's first-ever breeding record at Berryessa. Nest construction and an occupied nest were reported at northwest Lake Hennessey June 30, 1991. By August 1 there were 21 occupied nests and several adults with young on August 24. The report of an adult carrying food on the western shore of Lake Berryessa on October 22 is a very late confirmation. Five probable reports include courtship June 5-8, 1991, in two additional Hennessey blocks and at northwest Berryessa. Reports of possible breeding came from another four Berryessa blocks, Lake Curry, two tidal marsh blocks, and small reservoirs southeast of Angwin and in Pope Valley.

The colonies at the two county breeding lakes have uncertain futures. Human activity at Berryessa presents an annual problem for Western Grebe, although a small colony is succeeding at Big Island. Human approach results in all colony members leaving the nest (Storer and Nuechterlein 1992), increasing chances of nest predation or abandonment. There is less traffic at Hennessey; however, low water levels can prevent nesting by reducing and stranding shoreline vegetation. Western Grebe is considered an irregular breeding species in the county.

CLARK'S GREBE
Aechmophorus clarkii

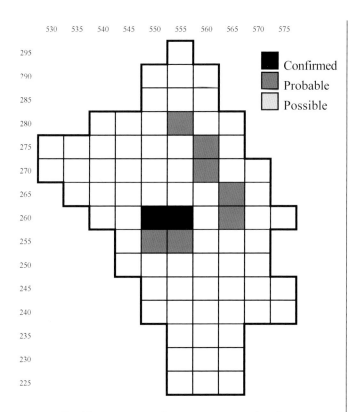

Confirmed
Probable
Possible

Resident year-round, more numerous in winter
Earliest confirmation June 30 - Nest with eggs
Latest confirmation July 21 - Precocial young

Among the rafts of grebes on Lake Hennessey or Berryessa during winter, perhaps one in 15 is a Clark's Grebe. And among the small number of Western Grebes that nest at the lakes, there are a few pairs of Clark's. The two grebes are nearly identical in their ritual breeding behaviors and habitat selection (Storer and Nuechterlein 1992) and were formerly regarded as a single species.

Clark's Grebe was confirmed in two Lake Hennessey blocks. At the Conn Creek arm of the lake, Ellen Sabine found a nest with eggs on June 30, 1991. At the mouth of Moore Creek on July 21, 1993, Andy and Lee Angel observed adults with young. The Conn and Moore sites supported two and five nests, respectively. In 1993 an additional 17 nests were occupied at Conn Creek. Birds observed displaying during June 1991 in the two southern Hennessey blocks were perhaps part of the confirmed breeding population along the northern shore. At Lake Berryessa during 1992 and 1993, mated and courting pairs were seen May 19-July 5. All observations were on the western shore, from upper Putah Creek south to Spanish Flat. Abundance was estimated at 11-100 pairs in each of the middle three of the five Berryessa blocks.

Atlas work represents the first nesting records in Napa County. At present, Clark's Grebe is considered an irregular breeding species. Variability in water level, extent of emergent vegetation, and human disturbance during a given year dictate breeding success.

DOUBLE-CRESTED CORMORANT
Phalacrocorax auritas

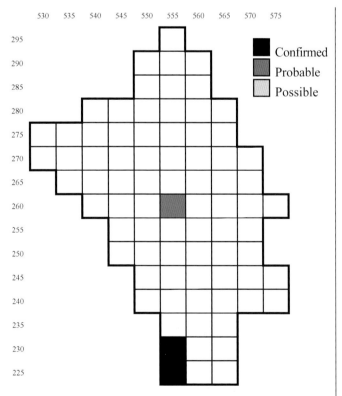

Year-round resident
Earliest confirmation May 12 – Occupied nest
Latest confirmation July 20 – Recently fledged young

Of the three West Coast cormorants, the Double-crested Cormorant is the only one that ventures inland to nest. In Napa County it does not venture far from the marine environment; Atlas and historic breeding records extend up the Napa River to Fly Bay and Buchli Station. Elsewhere, cormorants are found throughout the year at reservoirs across the county, but nesting is suspected only at Lake Hennessey. In Napa County cormorants nest in trees, specifically in drowned groves of eucalyptus adjacent to tidal sloughs and salt evaporation ponds. Nesting cormorants forage widely; e.g., birds nesting on the Farallon Islands have been found inside San Francisco Bay (Hatch and Weseloh 1999). Perhaps our tidal colonies also use the greater Bay to secure food for their young.

On May 12, 1989, an atlaser reported occupied nests at the small salt pond colony near Huichica Creek Wildlife Area. Fledglings were reported on July 20, 1991, in the block immediately to the north, an upland block that does not include river or tideland. At Lake Hennessey, several pairs of cormorants were found on May 28, 1993, representing the only probable breeding record. Non-breeding cormorants were observed in 21 additional blocks March 8-July 4.

The California population of cormorants is currently increasing, following DDT-era declines (Hatch and Weseloh 1999). The Huichica colony held 26 nests in 1986. Concurrent with removal and natural decay of eucalyptus in the tidal district, the number of nesting cormorants there will decrease.

24

GREAT BLUE HERON
Ardea herodias

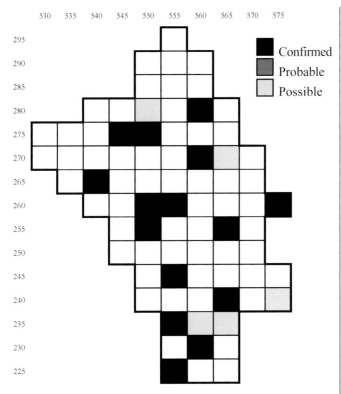

Confirmed

Probable

Possible

Year-round resident
Earliest confirmation February 17 – Nest building
Latest confirmation July 18 – Feeding young

Anyone who has paused along the southeastern part of Lake Hennessey late in spring may have seen the large stick nests of the Great Blue Heron in foothill pines on the opposite shore. An adaptable species, it nests near both fresh and salt water (Butler 1992). Of the Bay Area's four large Ardeids, it is the most likely to nest in forest habitat (Kelly *et al.* 1993). Locally, streams and reservoirs provide the great blue with foraging opportunities, and nesting is a possibility where large trees are present. Overall breeding bird density in the tidal district is low.

Great Blue Herons were building nests on Feb. 11, 1990, at a rookery supporting 21 nests near Napa Valley Country Club. Occupied nests were seen at nine locations March 11-June 16, and fledglings were present in four blocks between May 5 south of Napa and July 18 at Lake Hennessey. The two Pope Valley blocks each reported 11-100 nests, with the westernmost block supporting two rookeries. Seven nests fledged 15 young at Lake Hennessey in 1993. Seven blocks supported 2-10 pairs, including at least two in the Napa Valley, two in the tidal district, and one at Lake Berryessa.

Grinnell and Wythe (1927) mention a small rookery near Napa in 1901. Rookeries remain small and the county's population is concentrated at Pope Valley, Lake Hennessey, and near Napa Valley Country Club. Limiting disturbance and maintaining quality foraging habitat are critical to the nesting Great Blue Herons of Napa County.

Sponsored by Fran Scarlett

GREAT EGRET
Ardea alba

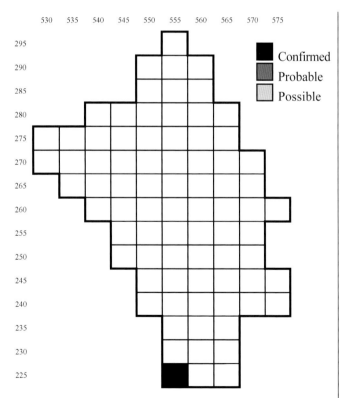

Confirmed

Probable

Possible

Year-round resident
Only confirmation July 1 – Nest with young

The Great Egret is one of the four colonially nesting, large wading birds of the San Francisco Bay Area. Once "reduced to a condition of rarity" (Grinnell and Miller 1944), its recovery is ongoing. The bay rookeries are located in a variety of shrub, wetland, and forest communities. In the North Bay, the lakes, marshes, creeks, and sloughs within the Napa River watershed provide important foraging habitat for each species (Kelly *et al.* 1993). During the Atlas, the Great Egret proved to be the rarest of our breeding Ardeids: a single nest was found representing the first Napa County breeding record.

Discovered by David Takeuchi at Huichica Creek Wildlife Area on June 13, 1992, the nest contained three young on July 1. It was in a dead eucalyptus tree that also held the nest of a Great Blue Heron, located along a brushy levee that divided intact tidal marsh to the west from an expanse of brackish lagoon and salt evaporator ponds to the east. Reports of non-breeding egrets during the Atlas span May 15-July 18.

Since the completion of the Atlas, Great Egret has been reported nesting among the Snowy Egrets and Black-crowned Night-Herons at the rookery at Napa State Hospital. That rookery is believed to be one of only two in the greater Bay Area where the three species nest together (pers. comm., R. Leong).

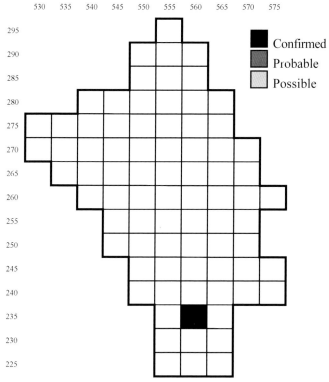

Year-round resident
Only confirmation May 15 – Nest with young

Confirmed
Probable
Possible

Napa County's first and only Snowy Egret colony was discovered as a direct result of the Atlas project. An atlaser investigating a traditional Black-crowned Night-Heron site at Napa State Hospital found five pairs of Snowy Egrets on the hospital grounds. On June 19, 1992, young were seen in two nests, and adults were adding nesting material as well. By July 1, five nests were believed active in a single live oak. During the summer of 1993, the colony had increased to 15 nests.

Most of the Snowy Egret colonies in a northern San Francisco Bay study area were located on isolated islands lacking nearby foraging opportunities (Kelly *et al.* 1993). It is believed that the egret's energy expenditure seeking food is balanced by an island's relative security from predators. The Napa State Hospital site is more than a mile from marginal foraging sites at the Napa River and five miles from the more productive tidal marsh. The securely fenced and heavily trafficked hospital grounds may provide a relatively predator-free environment for nesting egrets and herons.

The state hospital site remains the lone colony in Napa County. In 2002, J. Maillard (pers. comm.) describes the colony as "expanding and thriving."

GREEN HERON
Butorides virescens

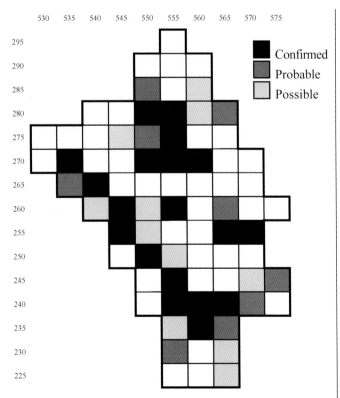

Year-round resident, rare in winter
Earliest confirmation April 15 – Nest building
Latest confirmation July 28 – Recently fledged young

An encounter with a Green Heron always seems to be a surprise for both the observer and the heron. Foraging for fish by day and in dim twilight, it is usually concealed amid dense thickets at the edges of lowland ponds and slow-moving streams. Green Herons often breed colonially, but where a territory can be defended, such as along a stretch of stream, a pair nests alone (Davis and Kushlan 1994). Widespread and fairly common during the summer, small numbers of these herons remain in the Napa Valley October-March.

The earliest confirmation is the lone nest building report, April 15 in north Napa. Southern Pope Valley reported eggs on June 12. Three occupied nests span May 3-July 1. Nestlings were in the Zinfandel block June 25 and at Pope Canyon July 4. Fledglings were found in 11 blocks between June 14 near Bothe and July 28 at Snell Valley. Probable reports of pairs at eight locations span April 15-July 11. In 23 blocks reporting abundance, 78 percent estimated 2-10 pairs; the balance reported single pairs.

The distribution of Green Heron demonstrates a decided preference for the county's major streams. Confirmations are contiguous along the Napa River between Calistoga and the city of Napa. Upper Putah Creek and Pope Valley form a second distinct concentration of breeding birds, and Capell Valley supports a few pairs. The remnant Napa Valley riparian corridor and the forested streams of the interior are essential to the continued presence of breeding Green Herons in Napa County.

BLACK-CROWNED NIGHT-HERON
Nycticorax nycticorax

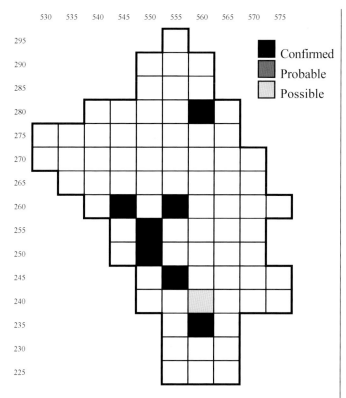

Confirmed
Probable
Possible

Year-round resident
Earliest confirmation May 10 – Nest with young
Latest confirmation August 6 – Feeding young

The most abundant bird in Napa's largest rookery is the Black-crowned Night-Heron. The colony at Napa State Hospital commonly supports more than 100 pairs, and the success of Night-Herons may have enticed Snowy and Great Egrets to nest there in recent years. Night-Heron foraging habitat is extremely varied and includes both fresh- and salt-water wetlands (Davis 1993). Herons at the Napa rookery probably use the entire river and marsh system below town to provide food for nestlings. Outside the breeding season, Night-Herons also roost communally. Day roosts of over 100 birds have been found within one mile of the hospital rookery.

Nests at the state hospital colony are placed in old growth coast live oak. During May 1993 nestlings were reported in some of the 122 active nests. Up the Napa Valley at Oakville, nestlings were seen on May 10, 1991. Fledglings were seen at the mouth of Eticuera Creek, Lake Hennessey, and in three Napa Valley blocks May 25-August 6. Probable breeding was reported in northwestern Napa May 29 where 2-10 pairs were present. The Oakville and Hennessey blocks also reported 2-10 pairs; the two other Valley blocks each held a single nesting pair. Non-breeding observations span April 7-July 26.

Despite continuing human presence at the rookery, the Napa State Hospital provides a very stable environment for Black-crowned Night-Herons (J. Maillard, pers. comm.). Of equal importance, nearby wetlands provide productive foraging opportunities. Elsewhere in the county, marginal and degraded wetland habitats support fewer birds.

29

TURKEY VULTURE
Cathartes aura

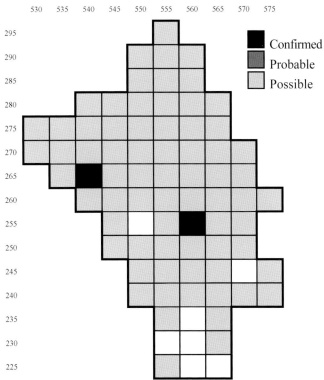

Confirmed
Probable
Possible

Year-round resident
Earliest confirmation May 25 – Nest with young
Latest confirmation July 8 – Recently fledged young

The Turkey Vulture is our noble scavenger. It attends to the dead in a matter-of-fact manner, exemplifying the ideal that death is part of life. Vultures forage over the entire county: canyons, forests, marsh, fields, and vineyards. They rest or roost on rock outcrops, canyon walls, among oaks, or upon a skeletal Douglas fir. In western North America, 91 percent of 309 nests studied were on rock cliffs or slopes (Kirk and Mossman 1998). Several Napa County nests have been found in tree stumps and rock crevices in closed canopy forest.

Grinnell and Wythe (1927) report eggs in California between April 9 and late May; Kirk and Mossman (1998) describe a similar interval. Turkey Vulture nestlings were discovered near Bothe on May 25, 1990. Fledglings were found northeast of Atlas Peak on July 8. The 76 additional records span February 26-July 11, probably illustrating the vulture's wide-ranging foraging behavior rather than actual breeding distribution. Confirmations may have been more widespread with greater coverage during July when fledglings are more conspicuous.

Turkey Vultures will remain a ubiquitous presence. Their needs are basic and well met throughout Napa County. However, as with almost every bird species, increased residential and agricultural development in remote areas of the county will impact breeding vultures. Kirk and Mossman (1998) stress the importance of a nest site isolated from human disturbance. Foraging opportunities for vultures throughout Napa County are diminished by the reduction of upland livestock grazing and the conversion of lowland pastures to other uses.

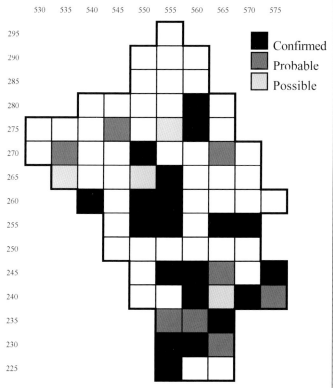

530 535 540 545 550 555 560 565 570 575

295
290
285
280
275
270
265
260
255
250
245
240
235
230
225

■ Confirmed
▨ Probable
□ Possible

Year-round resident
Earliest confirmation March 28 – Occupied nest
Latest confirmation July 18 – Recently fledged young

Once only a winter visitor to the northern Bay Area, the Canada Goose has become a resident of the region in the past 50 years. As a breeding species, it has responded favorably to changes in the distribution of fresh water and food availability and is tolerant of human presence. The subspecies that breeds in Napa County is the Great Basin form, *B.c. moffitti* (J. Swanson *fide* R. Leong).

Lake Hennessey supplied the earliest confirmations: an occupied nest March 28 and nest building April 6. Adults with young provided confirming breeding evidence in 15 blocks. The first reports of young were from Lake Hennessey on May 3 and in two southwestern blocks May 8. Nine such records span May 3-June 2. The latest observation of goslings was at northwestern Lake Berryessa on July 18. All probable records refer to pairs April 1-May 8. Estimates of abundance ranged from 1-10 pairs in 16 blocks. Wooden Valley, eastern Capell Valley, and the lower Carneros Valley each reported 11-100 pairs.

Napa's breeding Canada Geese are found at larger reservoirs, the smaller interior valleys, and along the Napa River from Oak Knoll south to Edgerley Island. Currently available fresh-water habitat may well be at carrying capacity. Except for parts of the Napa River reclamation effort, little additional breeding habitat is likely to be created, and the resident population will probably remain at relatively low levels.

WOOD DUCK
Aix sponsa

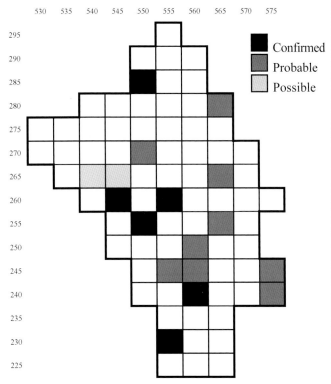

Year-round resident
Earliest confirmation June 1 – Recently fledged young
Latest confirmation July 11 – Precocial young

Confirmed
Probable
Possible

Resident year-round, the Wood Duck seeks seclusion in the wooded shadows of the county's reservoirs and streams. Never easily found, woodies use relict stretches of the Napa River and the smaller valley streams where large trees provide nest sites and dense cover serves to shelter the brood. Upland reservoirs such as Milliken and Berryessa may also support a few pairs, especially in the cover and quiet water where a stream feeds the reservoir. Since all confirmations were of fledgling broods, it is unknown whether Wood Duck used nest boxes during the Atlas.

Observations of fledglings in and near the Napa Valley span June 1-30 and include two mid-Valley records, one each in northeast Napa city, the Carneros district, and Lake Hennessey. A July 11 confirmation came from upper Putah Creek. Atlasers found mated pairs at Lake Berryessa and Lake Curry, in Pope, Capell, and Gordon Valleys, and in the Valley northwest of Napa.

The available breeding habitat and the population of Wood Duck are both reduced to remnants in Napa County. E. L. Bickford (1932) heard of them as "exceedingly abundant in pioneer days" on the Napa River but did not see one in the 20th century until 1925, when 26 birds wintered at "Little Trancas." Wood Duck formerly nested at the Napa River Ecological Reserve, where several pairs still winter annually. However, it was not found there during the Atlas period. The continued presence of this beautiful duck in Napa County depends upon protecting and restoring breeding habitat wherever possible.

Sponsored by Eleanor Dommerich

GADWALL
Anas strepera

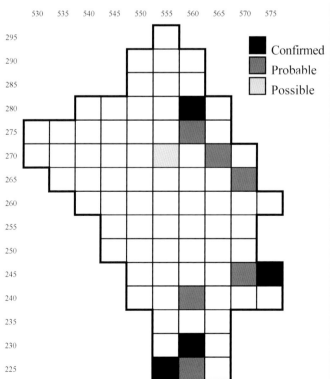

Primarily a winter resident, rare in summer
Earliest confirmation May 16 – Precocial young
Latest confirmation July 27 – Recently fledged young

The Gadwall is a duck of distinction, presenting an unmistakable silhouette across the water of the male layered in silver, black, and gray. Gadwall is common on open water during winter, and a few pairs remain in the county to nest near fresh-water lakes and ponds. Wetlands with tall emergent vegetation are favored, nests are preferentially placed on islands, and eggs are laid April-July (Bent 1923, Kortright 1953, Leschack *et al.* 1997).

The six probable Atlas reports describe mated pairs April 13-June 19. Pairs were seen at Lake Berryessa May 2-18, and Gadwall was confirmed on the lake at the mouth of Eticuera Creek where precocial young were seen on May 16. In the southern marshes, fledglings were found at Huichica Creek Wildlife Area on June 18 and at the Soscol Ferry Road water treatment facility July 27; mated pairs were present in a third southern block. Ducklings were discovered at Lake Curry on July 6. Additional reports came from ponds in Pope Valley, the north edge of the city of Napa, and in Wooden Valley. In the south abundance was estimated at 11-100 pairs in two blocks and 2-10 in the third. Lake Curry likewise estimated 2-10 pairs.

Prior to the Atlas, Gadwall had been confirmed nesting only at Huichica Creek in 1986 (eggs June 13), and Lake Hennessey in 1988 (precocial young June 22). There are additional records of summering individuals at Stanly Ranch and the Soscol Ferry Road water treatment facility.

MALLARD
Anas platyrhynchos

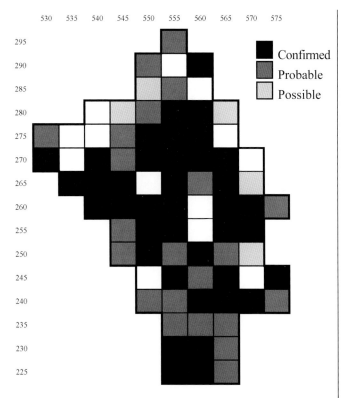

530 535 540 545 550 555 560 565 570 575

■ Confirmed
▨ Probable
▢ Possible

Year-round resident
Earliest confirmation April 22 – Distraction display
Latest confirmation July 26 – Recently fledged young

It is the unusual body of water, indeed, that does not host a pair of nesting Mallards. Tiny ponds, a bit of a stagnant stream, large lakes and marshes all support the Northern Hemisphere's most familiar duck. Nests are placed in dense upland vegetation, from grassland to woodland, often far from water. Brood-rearing waters usually have at least some cover vegetation. Mallards typically breed at fresh-water sites; however, broods have been seen in brackish water in the tidal district. Prior to the Atlas, egg dates representative of the early part of the season include four records at the Napa River Ecological Reserve, March 14-25.

Four nests were found during the Atlas, including nests with eggs on May 1 and 15 between St. Helena and Calistoga. The first of two April reports of precocial young came from Lake Hennessey on the 25th. There were 11 brood records during May and ten during both June and July. Dependent young were seen as late as July 26 at Putah Creek. The somewhat subjective distinction between the younger precocial and older fledged young divided about half the reports during each month, May-July. Probable records refer to pairs in breeding habitat, March 13-June 10.

The adaptable wild Mallard nests freely throughout the county. Equally free are the less wild birds, entirely habituated to life among people at reservoirs, parks, and golf courses. The distinction between the two blurs with time.

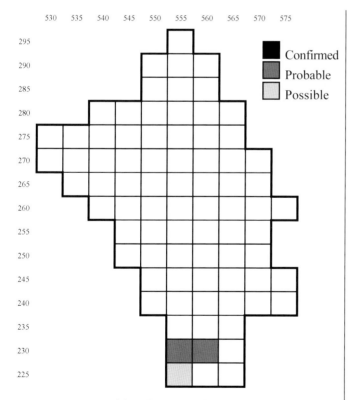

Confirmed
Probable
Possible

Very rare visitor, late winter/early spring
Earliest probable April 9 – Pair observed
Latest probable May 18 – Pair observed

Blue-winged Teal is the most abundant waterfowl in the interior of North America. It is the continent's second most common duck (Rohwer *et al.* 2002). In California, however, it is rare, and the presence of a pair in the Napa Marsh elicits at least mild excitement. Blue-winged Teal nests in upland cover near fresh-water wetlands. The breeding male is unusual among ducks in that he is intolerant of other males in his territory, allowing the females to proceed unmolested. Most male dabbling ducks exclude only females from the territory (Rohwer *et al.* 2002).

Blue-winged Teal were seen in three blocks during 1991. An observer found a mated pair and an individual teal, respectively, in two blocks near Buchli Station on April 9. A pair was discovered at the Soscol Ferry Road water treatment facility on May 18. The birds in each area were on small, artificial fresh-water ponds.

Outside of their normal range, Blue-winged Teal are known to breed opportunistically as conditions permit (Rohwer *et al.* 2002). Following the very wet winter of 1985-1986, a pair lingered May 18-June 1 at Huichica Creek Wildlife Area. Breeding was not confirmed. Teal continue to be seen occasionally in the county; there is at least one winter record of a male at Kennedy Park during January 1999.

CINNAMON TEAL
Anas cyanoptera

Napa's breeding Cinnamon Teal generally depart in autumn toward destinations as far south as Mexico. Scattered pairs are present throughout the winter; however, an almost imperceptible increase in numbers begins in February, and females are usually incubating eggs during the second half of April. Cinnamon Teal require dense perennial vegetation near fresh water for nesting (Gammonley 1996). Nests among sedge or rushes over water are "an unusual situation" (Bent 1925).

Atlas reports include two confirmations. Fledglings were seen at a wetland adjacent to the Soscol Ferry Road water treatment facility on June 15, 1991, and the observer estimated the presence of 11-100 breeding pairs in that block. Fledglings were also found at the Huichica Creek Wildlife Area on May 18, 1992. Mated pairs were reported in Coombsville on April 1, 1991, and at the mouth of Eticuera Creek on May 22, 1993. An individual adult was west of Napa Junction on May 26, 1991. The Coombsville and Eticuera Creek records are at locations where the species was unknown during the breeding season prior to the Atlas. The other sites are traditional; six historical records at Huichica Creek include young April 25-May 11 and eggs on May 1.

Fresh-water wetlands providing both brood cover and upland nest cover are few in Napa County. Opportunities to create such wetlands are limited by the availability of fresh-water inputs and by agricultural and industrial encroachment into most areas where the creation of such wetlands is possible.

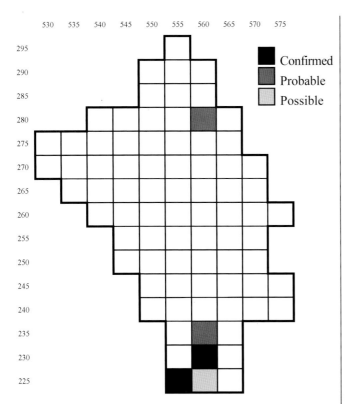

Year-round resident, at times absent December/January
Earliest confirmation May 18 – Recently fledged young
Latest confirmation June 15 – Recently fledged young

Sponsored by Nicholas Battiste and Dominique Battiste-Smith

NORTHERN SHOVELER
Anas clypeata

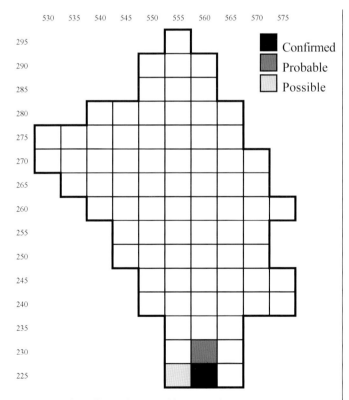

	■	Confirmed	
	▨	Probable	
	□	Possible	

Primarily a winter resident, rare in summer
Only confirmation June 24 – Recently fledged young

Following the torrential rains of early 1986, the area that was to become the Huichica Creek Wildlife Area was flush with fresh water well into the summer. During June the lingering wetlands produced the first Napa County breeding records of Northern Shoveler and Gadwall, a suspicious pair of Blue-winged Teal, and a number of other aquatic species rarely seen during the Napa summer. Common during winter, Northern Shoveler is otherwise quite rare in the Bay Area, with several counties in addition to Napa reporting first ever, or first "modern" breeding records between 1971-1995 (William G. Bousman, unpubl. data).

There was a single confirmation during the Napa Atlas. On June 24, 1991, Robin Leong found a female with young where sluggish, tule-lined Fagan Creek flows through hayfields just east of the Napa Airport. Several mated pairs were seen at the Soscol Ferry Road water treatment facility on May 19, 1990, and again on June 13, 1992. A single individual was at Huichica on April 11, 1990, the location of the first breeding record.

Northern Shoveler traditionally nests in grassland near fresh water (Dubowy 1996) and is known to nest at wastewater facilities in Marin and Sonoma counties (Campbell *et al.* 1985). The wetlands at Huichica have changed dramatically since 1986 and may no longer invite shovelers, regardless of winter rains. The water treatment facility and recovering wetlands adjacent to the Napa River may continue to host an occasional nesting pair.

NORTHERN PINTAIL
Anas Acuta

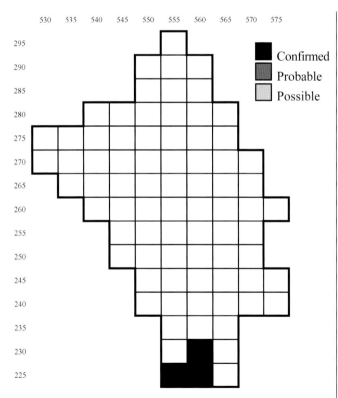

- ■ Confirmed
- ▨ Probable
- □ Possible

Primarily a winter resident, rare in summer
Earliest confirmation May 26 – Distraction display
Latest confirmation July 27 – Precocial young

The Northern Pintail is usually the least common of the puddle ducks that winter in the county. At best, a few pairs remain to nest, scattering across patches of fresh-water wetlands adjacent to the lower Napa River. Pintails are uncommon breeders in California, perhaps due to "low water permanency," but opportunistically take advantage of abundant winter rains, moving to breeding areas in March (Austin & Miller 1995).

The three blocks touching the Napa River south of Napa define the limits of nesting pintails in the county. Precocial young were found near the Soscol Ferry Road water treatment facility on July 27, 1990. An atlaser watched a female's distraction display at Cuttings Wharf on May 26, 1991, and fledglings at Huichica Creek on June 13, 1992. Each block was judged to support ten pairs or fewer.

Northern Pintail is not known to breed away from the three blocks described here. There are two records before 1989 at fresh-water ponds adjacent to the water treatment facility and one at Huichica Creek. The construction of the treatment facility in the 1970s created fresh-water habitat over diked ponds previously flooded by the tides. In addition, wastewater diversion has created vegetated wetlands near the facility.

The 1986 Huichica Creek record followed a winter of abundant rainfall, providing fresh water that persisted well into summer. Small areas of permanent fresh water have been created at Huichica since the establishment of the refuge. Reclamation of the Napa River floodplain may create habitat for Northern Pintail and the other rare puddle ducks.

COMMON MERGANSER
Mergus merganser

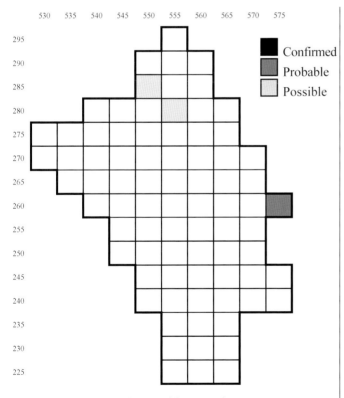

Confirmed
Probable
Possible

Uncommon winter resident, rare in summer
Only probable May 10 – Pair observed

If, as Grinnell and Miller (1944) describe, the Common Merganser prefers swift-flowing, wooded streams in the California summer, then its options are few in Napa County. The Napa River quickens in a few places, but only Putah Creek above Lake Berryessa provides a significant stretch of such habitat. Wooded lakes may also support breeding mergansers, and the many narrow inlets of Berryessa could serve to rear a brood. Mature trees are required for nest cavities, but Common Merganser is known to use rock crevices on the Pacific Coast (Bent 1923) and nest boxes throughout its range (Mallory and Metz 1999). Female mergansers commonly lead their broods downstream to larger waters in order to find sufficient food (Mallory and Metz 1999).

During the Atlas, Common Merganser was suspected of breeding only at Putah Creek and Lake Berryessa. Single birds were found on Putah Creek on July 11, 1991, and June 19, 1993, and a pair was seen above Monticello Dam on May 10, 1990. Since the conclusion of the Atlas, several large, potential nest trees at Putah Creek have fallen (R. Leong, pers. comm.).

Common Merganser regularly breeds in the north Coast Ranges, and Breeding Bird Survey results show a positive trend in California, 1966-2000 (Sauer *et al.* 2001). There is one historic breeding record in the county from upper Putah Creek.

RUDDY DUCK
Oxyura jamaicensis

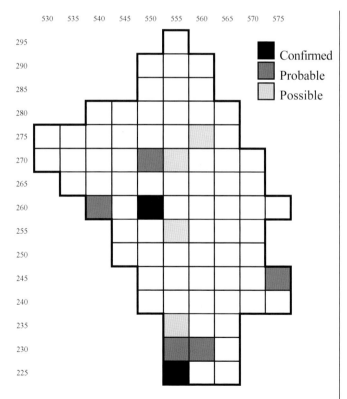

Year-round resident
Earliest confirmation June 5 – Nest with eggs
Latest confirmation June 22 – Precocial young

Confirmed
Probable
Possible

Only its large numbers distinguish the Ruddy Duck during the winter in Napa County. But as the breeding season approaches, the male ruddy is transformed into a russet and blue marvel prepared to dazzle his mate with elaborate courtship display. For her part, the female produces an egg that is larger than ducks three times her size (Kortright 1953). Nests are built over fresh water amid tall emergent vegetation adjacent to open water (Baicich and Harrison 1997).

Except for a June 8 Lake Hennessey report, possible records of individual Ruddy Ducks were concentrated during mid-May. A courting pair was at St. Helena on May 15, and pairs were found in four additional blocks June 13-18. In 1991 a nest with eggs was discovered at Lake Hennessey on June 5; precocial young from a different nest were seen there on August 1. Young were found at Huichica Creek Wildlife Area on June 22, 1993. An additional breeding record came from the mouth of American Canyon Creek in a non-priority block. A female accompanied seven ducklings at a fresh-water mitigation pond there on June 27, 1992.

Grinnell and Miller (1944) described the breeding population of Ruddy Duck in California as "reduced by reason of disappearance of appropriate breeding conditions." In southern Napa County, breeding Ruddy Ducks are found exclusively at small wetlands created since 1975. Elsewhere, they summer at a select few interior valley ponds and large reservoirs.

Sponsored by Stephanie Battiste

OSPREY
Pandion haliaetus

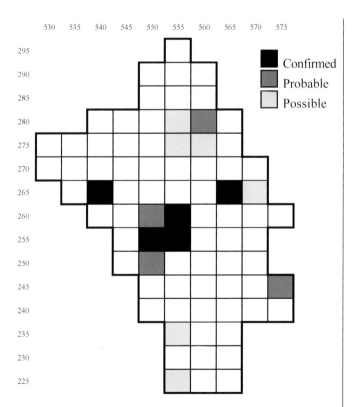

Confirmed
Probable
Possible

Year-round resident, fewer present in winter
Earliest confirmation April 30 – Nest building
Latest confirmation July 18 – Recently fledged young

The favorite Napa County fishing spot of the Osprey is Lake Hennessey. It is a year-round resident there, and birds annually occupy at least two nests in foothill pines near the shore. Osprey requires "reasonably clear and calm" water inhabited by surface-feeding fish (Ferguson-Lees and Christie 2001) and has been observed foraging over the slow, deep pools of the Napa River between St. Helena and Yountville. Pairs attempting to nest in the Napa Valley may be partly dependent on this limited resource.

Osprey was confirmed each year of the Atlas and successfully fledged young in at least four blocks. Birds added to nests in the northern Napa Valley April 30 and at Lake Berryessa May 30. Lake Hennessey reports included nestlings May 15 and fledged young July 18. Osprey nested in three Lake Hennessey blocks during the Atlas. In addition, a nest was built and occupied atop a wind machine in the Valley just southwest of the lake. Mated pairs were at Lake Curry, northeast Lake Berryessa, and Oakville between May 5-22.

Osprey suffered serious, DDT-related declines in North America after 1950. As contaminant levels have been reduced, Osprey has recovered most of its historic distribution and Lake Berryessa currently supports 15 active nests. Available food resources may be the limiting factor for the local population. In Wisconsin the growing population of Bald Eagles has recently begun to usurp Osprey nests. As eagles expand their nesting range to Lake Hennessey, it will be interesting to observe how the Osprey is affected.

WHITE-TAILED KITE
Elanus leucurus

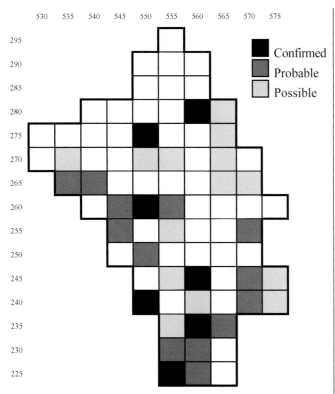

Year-round resident
Earliest confirmation March 20 – Carrying food
Latest confirmation June 27 – Recently fledged young

Confirmed
Probable
Possible

Our most graceful raptor, the White-tailed Kite is a resident of each of the county's valleys as well as the grasslands of the tidal district. Kites are "small mammal specialists," requiring a relatively small territory size that is apparently dependent on prey concentration and competitor abundance (Dunk 1995). Observations of communal winter roosts in the Napa Marsh include 45 birds at Knight Island on November 27, 1958. Longhurst (1959) suspected the roost represented the entire local population.

Mated pairs or territorial kites were reported the length of Napa Valley and at the interior valleys of Wooden and Capell February 20-June 25. Occupied nests were found in Conn Valley April 14, Edgerley Island May 8, and Pope Valley June 20. A nest with young was discovered at Kennedy Park June 15. Fledglings were just north of Napa May 15 and at Lake Berryessa June 27.

Following 1900, habitat loss, shooting, and egg collecting resulted in declines of California's kites (Dunk 1995). Although they recovered from those earlier abuses, more natural cyclical changes continue; an observed decline in California in the early 1990s (Dunk 1995) perhaps impacted Atlas results. Kites are also cyclical in their occupation of meadows within upland chaparral and oak woodland. Such sites above Rector Canyon, in southeastern Alta Heights, and in Wild Horse Valley have been sporadically occupied for the past 25 years. Development threatens these sites. Traditional areas lost since Atlas fieldwork ended include Lewis Dairy, derelict orchards at Chimney Rock, and Bale Lane.

          Sponsored by Richard Epstein

BALD EAGLE
Haliaeetus leucocephalus

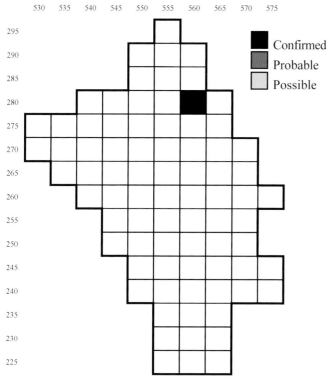

Year-round resident
Only confirmation April 29 – Nest with young

Confirmed
Probable
Possible

In the final decade of the 20th century the Bald Eagle at last nested in Napa County. At the time the Atlas was initiated, adult and juvenile eagles had become regular winter visitors at Lake Berryessa and Lake Hennessey. A nest attempted on the east side of Berryessa failed prior to 1989 and again in 1992, when a nest was built and abandoned. In 1992 a pair took over a Golden Eagle nest on the north side of Berryessa, and in 1993 it used the same nest. It fledged one young each year.

Bald Eagle usually nests in trees near water where fish, waterfowl, and carrion provide food. "Diurnal perch habitat" - tall, accessible, "super-canopy" trees adjacent to shoreline foraging areas and away from human disturbance - is an important habitat feature (Buehler 2000). At Hennessey and Berryessa, isolated foothill pines provide such perch sites. Residency appears the norm in Northern California breeding pairs; eagles fledged here are believed to migrate north to coastal Canada and Alaska during their first fall, returning early the following year (Jenkins *et al.* 1999).

In 2000 Bald Eagle nested successfully at Lake Hennessey for the first time, and at present, there are about four nests annually producing young at Lake Berryessa. In 1997 California had a breeding population of 142 pairs, up from 52 in 1982; breeding habitat in Oregon and Washington may be approaching carrying capacity (Buehler 2000). Bald Eagle remains an Endangered Species in California and is Federally Threatened.

Sponsored by George Gamble

NORTHERN HARRIER
Circus cyaneus

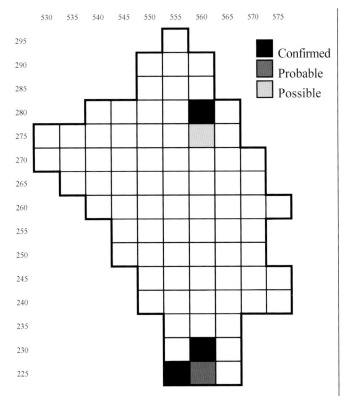

Confirmed
Probable
Possible

Year-round resident
Earliest confirmation April 27 – Occupied nest
Latest confirmation June 27 – Recently fledged young

The Northern Harrier is at once our most leisurely and animated raptor. It steadily quarters open country but then, in a sudden flourish, turns a tight cartwheel to pounce upon its prey. It rises from an idle perch to perform a sky dance of ascent and descent in accelerated, looping courtship. These small dramas play over open lands: tidal marsh, pastures, grassland, and lakeshores.

Harriers were found at the northern shores of Lake Berryessa and at the tidelands adjacent to the Napa River. An occupied nest was found in the Edgerley Island block on May 22, 1989. In a field of vetch and oat hay at the Napa Airport, a pair defended a nest with four eggs on April 27, 1991. A mated pair was seen in a third southern block on June 19, 1989. At Berryessa, fledglings were discovered at the mouth of Eticuera Creek on June 27, 1992; a lone, possible breeding bird was just to the south on May 18, 1993. A harrier east of Eticuera on May 5, 1993, was judged a non-breeding observation, as was a bird in Conn Valley on March 17, 1989.

Historically, nesting had been documented only in the extreme south of the Napa Marsh, near the Soscol Ferry Road water treatment facility and at Huichica Creek Wildlife Area. Because harriers that nest in marshes forage over grassland (Grinnell and Miller 1944), it will benefit this raptor if marsh and river reclamation plans favor the maintenance and recovery of grasslands.

SHARP-SHINNED HAWK
Accipiter striatus

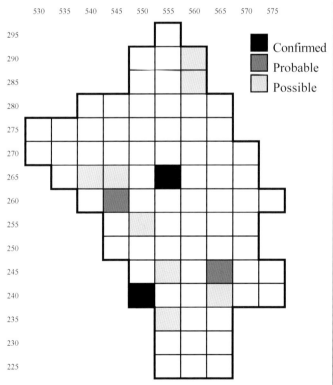

	Confirmed
	Probable
	Possible

Year-round resident
Earliest confirmation March 27 – Occupied nest
Latest confirmation July 18 – Recently fledged young

The Sharp-shinned Hawk is the most elusive of the diurnal raptors breeding in Napa County. The lone historic breeding record is a May 9, 1934, discovery of a nest with eggs at Martin Springs near Angwin, and summer reports of any kind were rare prior to the Atlas. Wintering Sharp-shinned Hawks can be found almost anywhere, and breeding birds forage widely as well, with the male providing all of the food for the incubating female and then for the female and young until the brood can be left alone (G. Jacobs, pers. comm.). Nests are usually placed in conifers, often in dense trees in mixed forest. Nest groves are commonly occupied from year to year, but the nest is not necessarily reused (Platt 1974).

In 1993 Sharp-shinned Hawk was confirmed in two priority blocks: fledglings above Chiles Valley on June 9, and at Redwood Canyon July 24. A nest containing three 13-day-old downy young was discovered in a non-priority block west of Calistoga June 18, 1993. Possible data is represented by individuals seen May 16-July 7, with six such records during 1990. Probable reports include a pair at St. Helena on April 4 and courtship activity on April 24 at Milliken. Pairs are known to frequent the nest area up to one month prior to egg laying (Platt 1974).

The legion of atlasers in the field found Sharp-shinned Hawk in unexpected numbers. Reports have increased at Bothe since 1995; however, the county-wide status and distribution remain poorly understood.

COOPER'S HAWK
Accipiter cooperii

ZEV-96

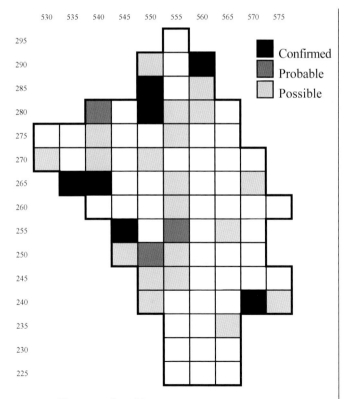

Confirmed
Probable
Possible

Year-round resident
Earliest confirmation May 10 – Occupied nest
Latest confirmation July 12 – Recently fledged

Cooper's Hawk is an uncommon resident of Napa County. Widespread during the winter, it becomes more localized during the breeding season. Nesting pairs are usually found in dense mixed forests or, less frequently, in the lower stretches of the larger canyons and along riparian corridors. An upland territory between Dry Creek and Pickle Canyon was occupied annually, 1980-1988. California nests are most often placed in oaks (Rosenfield and Bielefelt 1993). Feathers plucked from Northern Flicker and Steller's Jay are common clues to the presence of this hawk.

The discovery of fledglings between July 9 and 12 provided five of the seven Cooper's Hawk confirmations. Additional breeding records include a nest with young near Knoxville on May 25 and an occupied nest south of Calistoga on May 10. The three probable records include territorial or agitated birds, and one pair. All of the possible data refers to individuals in potential breeding habitat between March 20 and July 31.

Cooper's Hawk is most common west of a line from Yountville north to Knoxville, but nowhere in the county is it an easy bird to find during the breeding season. The nesting adults are quite secretive; it was the noisier fledglings that revealed most of the successful territories during the Atlas. Nesting pairs may be more widespread. Extensive research revealed the true abundance of this species in the upper Midwest of the USA (Rosenfield & Bielefelt 1993), which resulted in Cooper's Hawk being removed from the threatened list in Wisconsin.

RED-SHOULDERED HAWK
Buteo lineatus

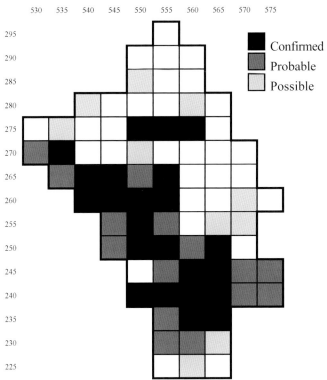

Year-round resident
Earliest confirmation March 27 – Occupied nest
Latest confirmation July 18 – Recently fledged young

The Red-shouldered Hawk maintains its historic presence as a year-round resident of riparian corridors and in forested upland habitats. It has also thoroughly adapted to the inside edges of the cities and towns of Napa Valley. It hunts the ditches of congested Imola Avenue, nesting in the oaks of golf courses and the eucalyptus groves of Coombsville and Rutherford. Partly dependent on an amphibian diet, it generally avoids areas without permanent water.

Probable breeding reports illustrating the early part of the season include mated pairs and territorial behavior at seven sites February 22-April 5. Nest construction was noted in three blocks March 27-28 and in two May 1-2. Nine occupied nests were found March 27-May 15. Nests with young were discovered near Foss Valley May 15 and Deer Park May 17, and at Wild Horse Valley on June 25. Fledglings were found at six locations between May 1 at Oakville and July 18 at northwestern Lake Berryessa. Historical data (1984-1988) includes nestlings at Napa River Ecological Reserve May 14-June 20 and fledglings in and near Napa May 9-June 27.

Except for a cluster of blocks between Pope Valley and Lake Berryessa, Red-shouldered Hawks appear to have settled most firmly in a broad area surrounding the city of Napa, as well as along the length of the Napa Valley and adjacent uplands. Continued success in these settled areas is assured only as long as nearby foraging sites remain available and where large trees are preserved in which pairs may construct a nest.

Sponsored by Alan Ringard, DDS

RED-TAILED HAWK
Buteo jamaicensis

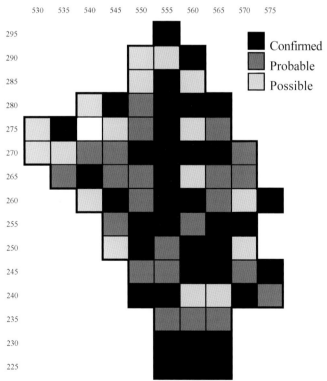

■	Confirmed	
▨	Probable	
▢	Possible	

Year-round resident
Earliest confirmation March 9 – Occupied nest
Latest confirmation September 7 – Recently fledged young

The most common and well-known diurnal raptor in California and much of the West, the Red-tailed Hawk is a resident species throughout Napa County. The subspecies found here, *B.j. calurus*, ranges from light to dark morphs. In western North America, the breeding population is greatest in the foothills of California, and this region hosts high concentrations of wintering birds (Preston and Beane 1993). Breeding habitat in Napa varies from marsh and rangeland in the south, to the Napa Valley floor, and up into the blue oak ridges of the northeast. Requiring open areas in which to hunt, Red-tailed Hawk is uncommon in the forested western hills and the higher elevations of the northwest.

Red-tailed Hawk was absent from only one priority block, around Sugarloaf Mt. west of Aetna Springs. Hawks carried nesting material near Redwood Canyon March 15 and near Bothe June 6. Seventeen occupied nests were found between March 9 and May 10, and nestlings were discovered in four blocks April 15-July 3. Nine fledgling dates span May 5-July 18. The observation of mated pairs accounts for 61 percent of all probable reports. Atlasers estimated 2-10 pairs in 31 of the 39 blocks reporting abundance.

The map shows that breeding evidence is strongest in the southern edge of the county and in the interior foothills east of the Napa Valley. In terms of fewer confirmations, breeding evidence was weaker across the one or two tiers of blocks of the northwestern border, Lake Berryessa's margins, and near the city of Napa.

GOLDEN EAGLE
Aquila chrysaetos

ZEV

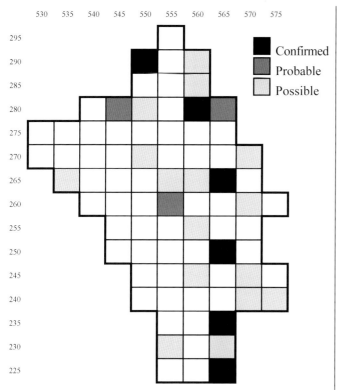

Confirmed
Probable
Possible

Year-round resident
Earliest confirmation March 19 – Occupied nest
Latest confirmation May 31 – Nest with young

The Golden Eagle is a resident of the mountain and ranch country of eastern Napa County. An eagle's prey, primarily small mammals and large birds, is concentrated in open wooded areas and grassland. A pair at Coombsville dines on Canada Goose goslings and regularly harasses Wild Turkey poults (A. Smith, pers. comm.). Adults are mostly sedentary, while juveniles disperse long distances and do not reach adulthood until their sixth year (Ferguson-Lees and Christie 2001).

The tradition of breeding in Napa County is strongest in Jamieson Canyon, and an occupied nest there on March 19, 1990, was the first Atlas confirmation. In 1991 nestlings were found near Wild Horse Valley Rd. on May 31. During 1992 a nest with eggs was discovered at Cedar Creek on April 27; nestlings were observed at northern Lake Berryessa and near Spanish Flat, both on May 3; and adults were feeding fledglings southeast of Atlas Peak on the approximate date of May 15. In 1993 mated or courting pairs were found at Lake Hennessey on January 26, west of Snell Valley on March 15, and at Blue Ridge on May 2. Possible breeders were soaring over an additional 16 blocks March 20-June 29.

Fowler (1900) was aware of Golden Eagles nesting near the summit of Mt. St. Helena in the 1890s. Don Hemphill discovered a nest on Howell Mt. in 1925. Atlas results reflect a current distribution confined to the relatively undisturbed east, where the population appears stable.

AMERICAN KESTREL
Falco sparverius

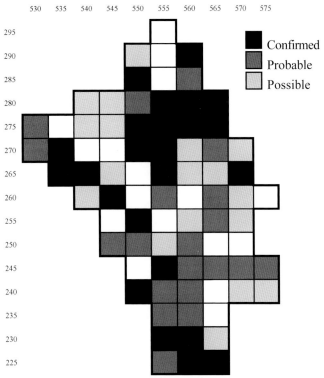

Year-round resident
Earliest confirmation April 16 – Occupied nest
Latest confirmation July 18 – Recently fledged young

Confirmed
Probable
Possible

The American Kestrel adds color and a little speed to the rural California landscape. Kestrels breed in a variety of open and woodland edge situations: pastures, oak savannah, lake shores, the edges of towns, and well-settled rural areas. Nests are placed in natural tree cavities, a crevice in a cliff or building, and in nest boxes. Nest boxes are usually readily accepted, and may provide the only suitable cavity at a given location or attract birds to habitat previously unoccupied (Bloom and Hawks 1983).

Mated pairs of kestrels were found in several blocks by early March. Observations of courtship and territorial behavior in eight blocks continued into July. The first of four reports of an occupied nest was in the lower Napa Valley on April 16 and the last at upper Putah Creek on June 28. Nestlings were first seen at St. Helena on April 22; the last of four records was at Calistoga on May 30. There were 15 fledgling reports: six during the period May 29-June 18 and nine between June 20-July 18. Observers reporting abundance in 29 blocks estimated 2-10 pairs in 22 of those blocks.

American Kestrels are adaptive falcons, occupying most areas of the county where sufficient open grassland-type foraging habitat exists. Nest cavities are often absent in even optimal habitat, however, and kestrels use boxes constructed for Wood Ducks in several parts of the county. Nest box programs benefit kestrels wherever attempted and would help maintain a secure future for them in Napa.

Sponsored by Joan Ferguson

PEREGRINE FALCON
Falco peregrinus

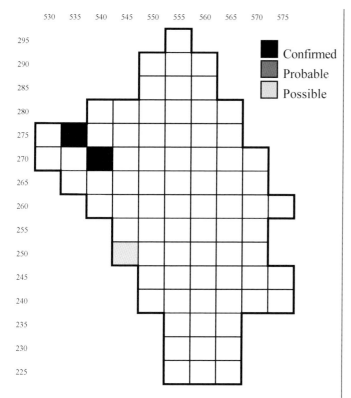

Confirmed
Probable
Possible

Year-round resident
Earliest confirmation May 12 – Nest with young
Latest confirmation June 6 – Nest with young

By 1970 the California population of Peregrine Falcon had dwindled to pairs attempting to nest at fewer than ten locations (Herman 1971), including the Palisades above Calistoga. The resident Palisades falcons endured and successfully raised young at two eyries during the Atlas period. Napa's Peregrines nest in cliff-face cavities and forage widely over the mountains and valleys, taking prey as large as ducks.

During the first year of the Atlas, an observer reported nestling Peregrines near Table Rock on June 6. In April 1992 an adult male courted a yearling female at Table Rock. On May 12-13, 1992, two atlasers investigated an eyrie at Dutch Henry Canyon, discovering four young in an old Red-tailed Hawk nest. The nestlings were judged to be 31 days old, indicating an egg date of March 13, believed to be the earliest ever in northern California. An individual Peregrine Falcon at Mt. St. John on June 7, 1989, represents a possible breeding location. A non-breeding bird was seen near Bothe on April 16, 1990.

In 1972 the pesticide DDT was banned in the United States. Later in the 1970s, the release of captive-reared falcons began. In 1999 the Peregrine Falcon was removed from Federal and State lists of Endangered or Threatened Species. It may be cautiously described as thriving in Napa County; active eyries in 2002 include five above the Napa Valley and one at Lake Berryessa. Peregrines may be seen throughout the year from the Palisades Trail.

Sponsored by John Boyd and Charlotte Kisling

PRAIRIE FALCON
Falco mexicanus

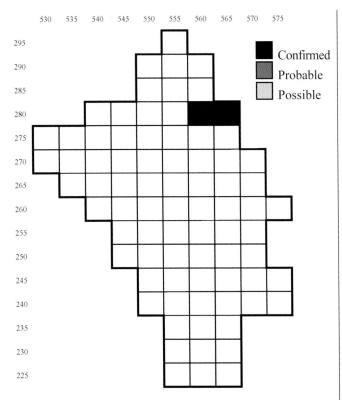

Rare year-round resident
Earliest confirmation April 1 – Occupied nest
Latest confirmation May 17 – Nest with young

The Prairie Falcon is a resident only at the Blue Ridge country rising from the northeastern shore of Lake Berryessa. The broken foothill woodland and open shore of the lake provide abundant foraging opportunities, and rock outcrops support the nest. Prairie Falcon food items vary by region; central California birds are known to exploit ground squirrels and meadowlarks (Fowler 1931), two species common at Berryessa. Northern California territories average 88 square miles and may be occupied for 30-plus years; the actual nest site often changes between years (Boyce *et al.* 1986, Steenhof 1998).

During the Atlas an observer confirmed Prairie Falcon in adjacent northeastern Berryessa blocks. Young were seen in the nest on May 17, 1992, and a second nest was occupied on April 1, 1993. Considering that an Atlas block is almost ten square miles, the two nests probably represent one territory. It is perhaps not an issue in our small population, but foraging territories can overlap between pairs (Steenhof 1998). An individual Prairie Falcon was observed south of Angwin July 7, 1989. There is a June 19, 1978, record of a nest with young nearby at the Palisades.

Prairie Falcon is more sensitive to DDT than Peregrine Falcon, but it did not suffer such catastrophic declines because of its lower trophic position on the food chain, i.e., it eats fewer birds (Jarman *et al.* 1996). In 1977 California had an estimated 300-500 breeding pairs (Boyce *et al.* 1986). Prairie Falcon is seen occasionally around the Napa Marsh during winter.

RING-NECKED PHEASANT
Phasianus colchicus

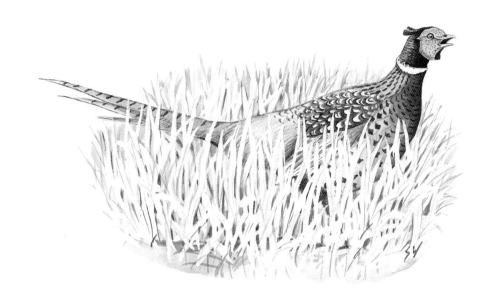

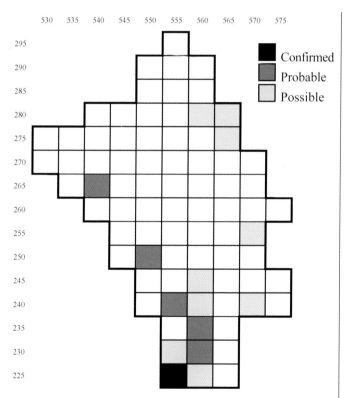

Year-round resident
Only confirmation July 2 – Recently fledged young

The Ring-necked Pheasant comes to Napa by way of Asia and Oregon. The first successful American introductions were in Oregon in 1881 (Bent 1932); the first attempts in California were in 1889, and by the 1930s populations were established throughout the Lower 48 (Giudice and Ratti 2001). While in general a grassland bird, the most successful pheasants require a mosaic of woodlot edge, brush, marsh, and multi-crop agriculture. Dense herbaceous cover is especially important for the nest and brood (Giudice and Ratti 2001).

The upland edges of the southern tidal marshes have long been the center of concentration in the county. One observer obtained the lone Atlas confirmation there: fledglings at Edgerley Island on July 2, 1989. Probable reports span May 5-18, all in the Napa Valley lowlands from the Napa airport to near Calistoga. Six possible records span May 3-26 and include birds in Wild Horse and Capell Valleys. There were two April 15 Lake Berryessa reports, and a pheasant was in Carneros on June 27. There are two historic egg dates from the Napa Valley: April 30 and May 7 at Calistoga and Yountville, respectively.

The distribution of Ring-necked Pheasant in Napa County has changed little since the population became self-sustaining. However, as is the case throughout North America (Giudice and Ratti 2001), its relative abundance has apparently declined. Available habitat continues to be reduced by development in the south and increasingly tidy viticultural practices in the Napa Valley.

WILD TURKEY
Meleagris gallopavo

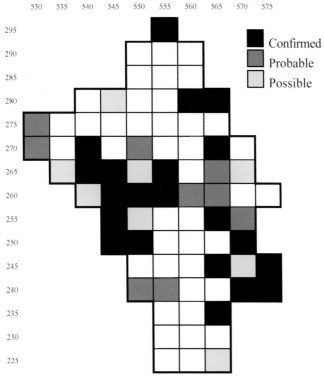

Confirmed
Probable
Possible

Year-round resident
Earliest confirmation May 14 – Precocial young
Latest confirmation August 21 – Recently fledged young

Attempts to establish Wild Turkeys in the county in the 1920s and 1930s failed, but at Pope Valley in 1970 the release of the "Rio Grande" strain from Texas was successful. More releases followed in Wooden Valley, near Lake Berryessa, and in other locations (Calif. Dept. of Fish & Game, historical information). Turkeys range over blue and black oak forest, dry open slopes, deciduous canyons, and open chaparral - often where foothill pine is present. Despite their extremely wary nature, they will visit backyards where feed is scattered. Wild Turkeys were found in almost one-half of Atlas priority blocks.

Atlas reports of courtship and mated pairs suggest that Wild Turkeys initiate the breeding season primarily during the middle one-third of April. Since the female incubates her clutch of eggs for 28 days (Baicich and Harrison 1997), four records of fledglings May 14-17 indicate a mid-April onset as well. The early records fall across the entire local range: Capell Valley, northern Lake Berryessa, and Conn Valley. Seventeen additional fledgling reports include 11 between May 28 and June 25, four during July, August 4 at Eticuera Creek, and August 21 west of Rutherford.

Wild Turkeys have spread widely from their original release points, reaching Knoxville, Mt. St. John, Skyline Park, and Rattlesnake Ridge. Turkeys are not found in pastureland or hard chaparral. Atlas records indicate that they are absent from all but the lowest density rural residential habitats. The species is not abundant; estimates tended toward ten or fewer pairs per block.

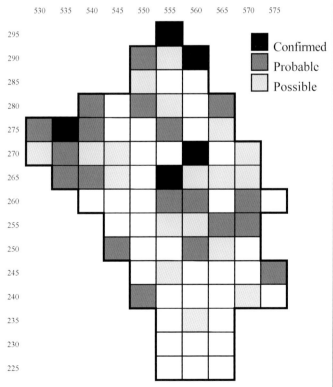

Confirmed
Probable
Possible

Year-round resident
Earliest confirmation June 3 – Precocial young
Latest confirmation July 14 – Recently fledged young

In the hills of Napa County, the Mountain Quail could also be called the "canyon quail," since it is so often heard calling from the other side of whichever canyon one happens to be visiting. It is partial to rocky, broken oak and chaparral slopes, usually with plenty of dense cover. Mountain Quail requires a source of free water year round (Gutierrez and Delahanty 1999) and nests from about 300 feet elevation at Rector Canyon to near 4000 feet on the slopes of Mt. St. Helena. Reproduction is "strongly influenced by winter and spring rainfall...in a Mediterranean climate" (Gutierrez and Delahanty 1999). Sufficient moisture provides this quail with the lush spring plant growth required for food and cover.

Mountain Quail can usually be heard during the earliest days of spring. Atlasers reported calling males in 21 blocks April 14-June 28, representing 57 percent of combined possible and probable data. Reports of territorial behavior or mated pairs in eight blocks span May 2-June 30. The five confirmations, all encounters with coveys of precocial young between June 3 and July 14, came from the Cedar Roughs, Knoxville, and Robert Louis Stevenson State Park.

Because seeing Mountain Quail at any season is difficult, a survey of calling males April-May provides a good representation of the breeding range. Quail may forgo breeding during dry years (Gutierrez and Delahanty 1999), and the persistent drought during the Atlas period may have influenced breeding success.

CALIFORNIA QUAIL
Callipepla californica

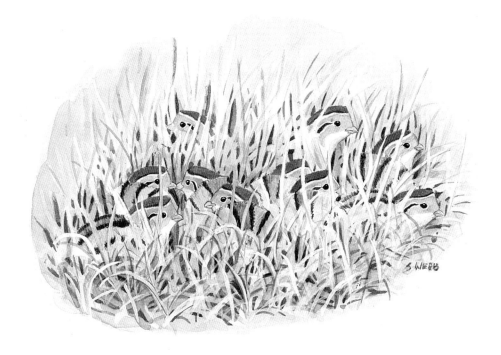

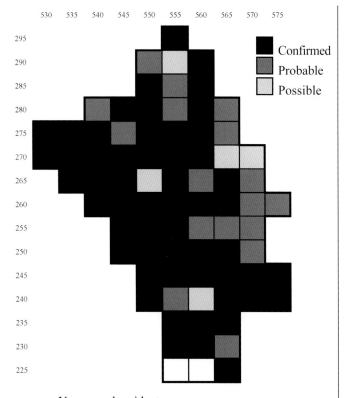

Confirmed
Probable
Possible

Year-round resident
Earliest confirmation March 17 – Recently fledged young
Latest confirmation September 7 – Recently fledged young

It is a marvel that such an endearing bird as the California Quail, and a game bird at that, survived the 20th century to share the state with 35 million human inhabitants. It is prolific: coveys of 100 are occasionally found in winter, and a pair leading a brood of 15-20 young is a common sight. It thrives in most chaparral habitats, riparian tangles, and open oak woodland. Quail are also common in lower density residential neighborhoods that are left a little wild. All habitats require areas of dense cover for concealment (Calkins *et al.* 1999).

Quail were confirmed in 55 priority blocks by the observation of broods exploring with their parents. There were nine records during the second half of May, 29 in June, and 13 in July. Young in Soda Canyon March 17, near Lake Hennessey August 24, and at St. Helena September 7 are probably incidental observations. Second broods, hatching in August, are known in productive years (Calkins *et al.* 1999). Such records have historical precedents in the county: fledglings at the Napa River Ecological Reserve August 20 and September 6, and at Bothe August 25. Egg dates in California span February 9-October 29 (Bent 1932).

Quail proved common throughout the county, including the heavily developed Napa Valley floor and the edges of towns and cities. Aggressively "clean" viticulture, with all potential quail cover removed, will adversely impact birds where it is practiced. Hunting is judged to have no effect on the population (Calkins *et al.* 1999).

Sponsored by Mt. Diablo Audubon Society

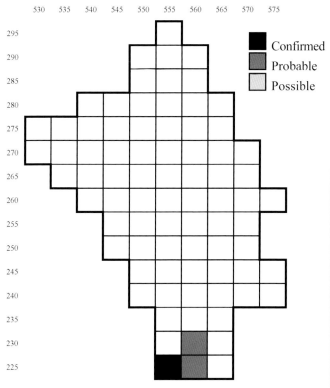

530 535 540 545 550 555 560 565 570 575

295
290
285
280
275
270
265
260
255
250
245
240
235
230
225

■ Confirmed
▨ Probable
□ Possible

Year-round resident
Only confirmation May 27 – Precocial young

Inhabiting inaccessible tidal marshes, the tiny and secretive Black Rail is a prized resident of the county's southern tidal district. In the spring it is relatively easy to locate during twilight by its distinctive call. State Threatened, the rail is "confined to the most pristine remnants of historical tidal marshes" (Evens *et al.* 1991). In 1986 the San Pablo Bay population was estimated at between 3200 and 8600 birds, and a 1991 survey determined that the rail is largely restricted to the northern reaches of San Francisco Bay (Eddleman *et al.* 1994). Marshes adjacent to the Napa River may support the majority of the North Bay population.

The efforts of an ornithologist with PRBO Conservation Science supplied the three Atlas records for Black Rail. Late February 1992, observations of agitated birds provided probable breeding evidence in two blocks. The species was confirmed on May 27, 1993, when precocial young were seen. These discoveries occurred between Fagan and Napa Sloughs west and southwest of the Napa Airport. The abundance of rails in each of the two blocks was estimated at 10-100 pairs.

Grinnell and Wythe (1927) do not mention Black Rail occurring in Napa Co., although it was certainly present. Throughout the 20th century, salt production, urban growth, and water quality issues affected rail populations. Today the salt industry is gone, the marshes are largely in public hands, and reclamation has begun. The prospects for Black Rail are improving.

CLAPPER RAIL
Rallus longirostris

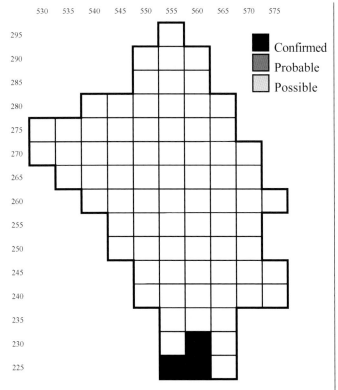

Confirmed
Probable
Possible

Year-round resident
Earliest confirmation February 24 – Used nests
Latest confirmation May 28 – Nest with eggs

The Clapper Rail is large and frequently noisy, living within the cover of remote tidal wetlands and usually impossible to see. Often, only conditions of extreme high or low tide will bring one into view. A sedentary species, clappers favor tidal sloughs with a dominant cover of pickleweed and cordgrass (Eddelman 1998). The Clapper Rail, State and Federally Endangered, has lost an estimated 80-90 percent of its nesting habitat in the greater San Francisco Bay (Eddelman 1998).

As with the Black Rail, research by PRBO Conservation Science allows inclusion of the Clapper Rail in Atlas records. During 1992, a used nest was found February 24; egg fragments, used nests, and an occupied nest were discovered May 16; and a nest with eggs was found May 28. These nests were located adjacent to the Napa River between Fagan and Napa Sloughs. The May 16 reports found rails in "youthful marshlands," primarily *Scirpus*, along the southeast margin of Coon Island. An abundance of 1-10 pairs was estimated for each block. It is important to note that the range of both the threatened Black Rail and the endangered Clapper Rail includes the same three Atlas blocks.

Apparently overlooked early in the 20th century (Grinnell and Wythe 1927), the Clapper Rail remains a difficult bird to find, owing to its scarcity, remote habitat, and secretive nature. It has endured threats similar to the Black Rail and shares the same promise for the future as the abuses of the past are healed.

In memory of John Applegarth

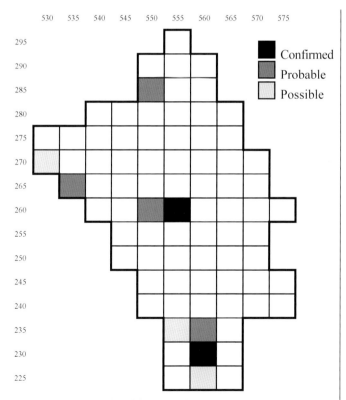

530 535 540 545 550 555 560 565 570 575

295
290
285
280
275
270
265
260
255
250
245
240
235
230
225

■ Confirmed
▨ Probable
☐ Possible

Year-round resident, rare in summer
Earliest confirmation June 6 – Recently fledged young
Latest confirmation June 8 – Recently fledged young

A common winter resident of southern marshes and sloughs, Virginia Rail abandons the salt in favor of fresh water during the breeding season. Less of a challenge to hear than its salt-water cousins, it is often more easily seen as well. Where both Sora and Virgina Rail arc present, the latter favors the drier portion of a marsh (Conway 1995).

Found at isolated locations the length of the Napa Valley from Calistoga south to the Napa Airport, six probable and confirmed reports span June 6-July 26. The two confirmed records are of fledglings June 8, 1991, along the Napa River just south of Napa, and June 6, 1993, at Lake Hennessey. The location of many of the records suggests that Virginia Rails attempt to nest at small irrigation ponds in the Valley. Territorial birds at a natural pond in the upper Putah Creek drainage and at Lake Hennessey are the only other reports away from the Napa Valley. Abundance estimates are fewer than ten pairs in all blocks reporting.

Atlas records indicate that fresh-water habitats supporting Virginia Rail are small and scattered; they are probably all at risk. For example, groundwater pumping has altered wetlands at the Napa River Ecological Reserve, the site of the lone historical breeding record. Irrigation ponds are routinely cleared of emergent vegetation. Drought strands shoreline-breeding habitat at larger reservoirs. Efforts to restore the Napa River floodplain may increase stable breeding habitat for Virgina Rail.

SORA
Porzana carolina

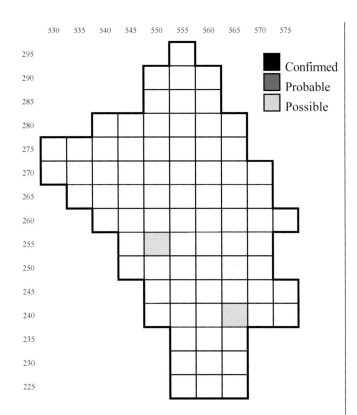

Winter resident, rare or absent in winter
Earliest possible April 8 – Singing male in habitat
Latest possible June 10 – Species in habitat

A fairly common winter resident of the tidal marshes, Sora mostly abandons the county during its breeding season. It is vocal at any time of day, especially when disturbed. During the breeding season Sora favors shallow fresh-water habitat where cattail and sedge grow (Melvin 1996). Sora frequently swims at the open edge of cover and is probably the easiest of the local rails to see well.

Atlas observations are limited to single birds at two sites: a calling individual was discovered at Conn Creek east of Oakville on June 10, 1991, and a calling male was found in Wild Horse Valley on April 8, 1992. In April 1975, a nest with eggs was found at Conn Creek, near the site of the Atlas observation. It is the lone county breeding record. Nesting habitat may still exist at densely vegetated lowland streams and at human-created wetlands such as irrigation ponds and possibly golf course lakes, but these sites are marginal at best.

During the breeding season Sora is strictly limited to fresh water with extensive emergent vegetative cover (Bent 1926). Suitable wetlands are scarce in Napa County. This continentally abundant rail may only exceptionally be expected to breed in Napa County.

COMMON MOORHEN
Gallinula chloropus

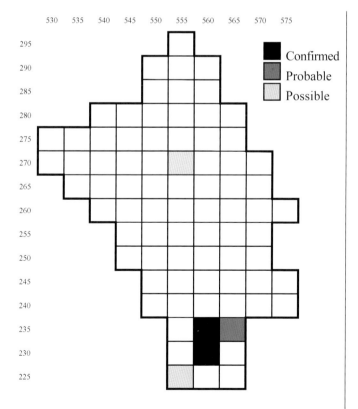

Confirmed
Probable
Possible

Year-round resident
Earliest confirmation May 2 – Recently fledged young
Latest confirmation June 15 – Occupied nest

While similar in appearance to the ubiquitous American Coot, the Common Moorhen, tending toward a solitary and retiring lifestyle, shares little in common with the coot. In Napa County the moorhen rarely ventures far from tule and cattail or low willow cover in small fresh-water ponds and marshes. The nest is usually placed over water (Bent 1926). A moorhen territory often includes additional nests that are used only for brooding the young (Baicich and Harrison 1997).

Common Moorhen was confirmed nesting at two unusual wetlands. On June 15, 1991, an atlaser observed an occupied nest at a flooded gas well grown up in tules along Aviation Way; and on May 2, 1993, two fledglings were found in the willows and tules of a rock quarry pond near Napa State Hospital. A pair of adults was present in Coombsville on May 6, 1992, and during 1993 individual adults were at Huichica Creek Wildlife Area on April 25 and at the Hardin Creek ponds in Pope Valley on May 21. Available habitat was judged to support 2-10 pairs in the confirmed blocks, and one pair in each of the other south county blocks.

The lone breeding record of Common Moorhen prior to the Atlas was at Lake Hennessey on June 15, 1980. Suitable fresh-water nesting habitat is rare in the county. As a consequence the moorhen, while present throughout the year, is equally rare, and successful nesting is a random, unexpected event.

AMERICAN COOT
Fulica americana

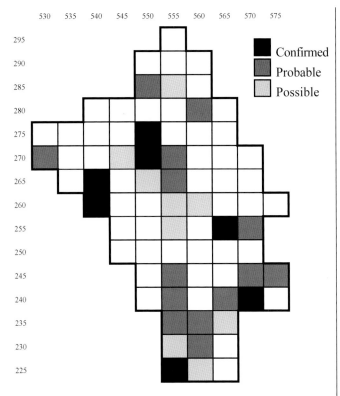

Year-round resident
Earliest confirmation May 27 – Feeding young
Latest confirmation July 12 – Recently fledged young

Confirmed
Probable
Possible

A member of the family of rails, the American Coot shares little of the mystery of its relatives hidden deep within the marsh. Hundreds winter on county reservoirs or gather on the lawns and ponds of parks and golf courses. Those that remain to breed select ranch ponds and irrigation reservoirs where sufficient emergent vegetation conceals a nest usually built over water. Coots often build extra nests to serve as resting or brooding platforms (Baicich and Harrison 1997).

During the Atlas, the one nest that was found contained eggs, at an upper Napa Valley pond on May 30, 1989. Fledglings or precocial young were found in six blocks: first at Pope Valley on May 27, last at Wooden Valley on July 12. The other four reports of young spanned June 13-20. Probable records refer to mated pairs through July 11 and to agitated suspected nesting birds through June 30.

The location of the majority of the strongest breeding evidence indicates that during the Atlas period American Coot nested on the smaller available fresh-water sites. There were single reports from each of the largest reservoirs: Berryessa, Hennessey, and Curry. During drought those lakes may lack the waterside vegetation required to raise young, and coots are not known to breed on the lakes; the two historical records are from Pope Valley and Napa Valley. Irrigation ponds, where the water level is maintained throughout the year, represent the most important breeding habitat for American Coot in Napa County.

Sponsored by Robin Leong

SNOWY PLOVER
Charadrius alexandrinus

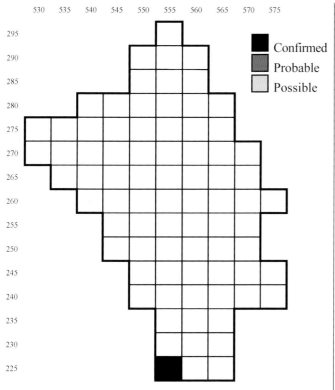

■ Confirmed
▨ Probable
□ Possible

Year-round resident
Only confirmation June 17 – Occupied nest

The Snowy Plover breeds in the northern middle latitudes throughout the world. From Portugal east to Japan, it is known as the Kentish Plover. The eastern Pacific population nests primarily on coastal beaches. Birds inside San Francisco Bay have adapted to nesting at salt evaporation ponds; as long ago as 1914, plovers had occupied such sites in Alameda County (Bent 1929). Montcrey County birds raise up to three broods, March-June, as the male tends the precocial young and the female initiates the subsequent clutch (Page *et al.* 1995).

At a Little Island salt evaporation pond on June 17, 1989, an observer located one pair of Snowy Plovers and their nest. Searches of the same site on June 16 and July 6, 1990, revealed a total of at least three nests. An egg was seen in one nest and adults appeared to be incubating eggs in the other two. All were situated on small, barren islands within the salt pond. Snowy Plovers are resident at the area's salt ponds and continue to nest. The first breeding record in the North Bay (Page and Stenzel 1981) was of three nests at a Little Island evaporation pond in 1975. Up to 26 birds have been seen during winter at salt ponds at Huichica Creek Wildlife Area.

It is estimated that there are 4000 Snowy Plovers on the Pacific Coast of the United States (Page *et al.* 1995). In California it is a Species of Special Concern. The entire West Coast population is Federally Threatened.

KILLDEER
Charadrius vociferus

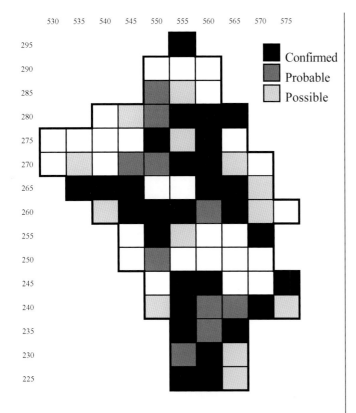

Year-round resident
Earliest confirmation April 4 – Occupied nest
Latest confirmation August 19 – Distraction display

Known to all, the Killdeer is familiar to anyone in California who has ever played golf, gazed upon a plowed field, or walked across a gravel parking lot. Prior to settlement, Killdeer probably nested on the gravel and sandbars of rivers and creeks, washouts, and recently burned-over sites (Jackson and Jackson 2000). Today, they exploit a variety of human-created habitats: rooftops, lake shores, grazed pastures, railroad beds, and barren levees. Despite their acceptance of human settlement, Killdeer still freak out when we get too near the nest or young, performing their famous "broken wing" distraction display in order to confuse intruders.

In fact, those displays represented 45 percent of all Atlas confirmations; 13 performances ran from April 16 south of Yountville through August 19 at Lake Hennessey. The latter record is at the outside edge of the breeding season; eggs are known in California March 15-July 2 (Bent 1929). Two occupied nests include the earliest confirmation at northeastern Lake Berryessa April 4, and nests containing eggs were discovered at six locations the length of the county May 8-June 25. Atlasers were treated to the sight of precocial young in eight blocks May 5-July 23. Abundance was described as 11-100 pairs in 15 blocks, perhaps an indication of just how much habitat we have created.

Killdeer are common near fresh water in the valleys and at reservoirs throughout the county, as well as in brackish and saltwater environments in the tidal district.

Sponsored by John O'Connell

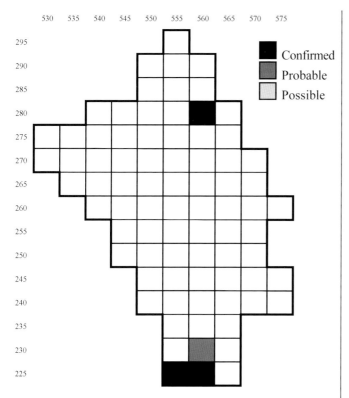

530 535 540 545 550 555 560 565 570 575

295 290 285 280 275 270 265 260 255 250 245 240 235 230 225

■ Confirmed
■ Probable
□ Possible

Year-round resident
Earliest confirmation May 12 – Occupied nest
Latest confirmation June 18 – Feeding young

Approaching the breeding territory of a Black-necked Stilt, one is instantly and incessantly urged to turn back as the pair sounds the alarm. Stilts always see you coming, since they nest on spits of mud and at the edges of salt evaporation ponds, open tidal wetlands, or flooded lowlands with minimal emergent vegetation. Stilts use both fresh- and salt-water wetlands and often breed in loose colonies (Robinson *et al.* 1999).

As expected, stilts were found in the three tidal marsh blocks adjacent to the Napa River: observers discovered adults feeding fledglings on June 18, 1989; an occupied nest was located on May 12, 1992; and a mated pair was observed on May 19, 1990. Historical records in this area include nests at Napa's water treatment facility mitigation ponds, salt ponds at Huichica Creek Wildlife Area, Napa River Reclamation District ponds on Milton Road, and Stanly Ranch. Although stilts were previously not known to breed away from the tidelands, one observer made the unprecedented discovery of a nest with eggs at the mouth of Eticuera Creek on May 22, 1993.

Black-necked Stilt currently breeds only in areas modified by human activity. Mitigated wetlands and reclaimed floodplain perhaps most closely mimic natural breeding sites. Grinnell and Miller (1944) described a great reduction in numbers commensurate with the reduction in the area of marshland in California. Since stilts use salt ponds for breeding, tidal marsh reclamation will have uncertain impacts on the population in that area.

Sponsored by Myrlee Potosnak

AMERICAN AVOCET
Recurvirostra americana

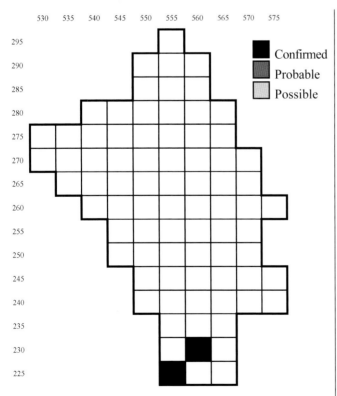

Year-round resident, more numerous in winter
Earliest confirmation May 26 – Recently fledged young
Latest confirmation June 20 – Occupied nest

During the winter season, large parading flocks of American Avocet are found in wetlands from Kennedy Park south to Slaughterhouse Point. In comparison, the breeding population is small, limited to several pairs at a few locations. Avocets nest primarily at brackish or salt water sites. Open lagoons or similar impoundments isolated behind levees from the full influence of tides are typical nest sites for birds in the southern marshes. Unlike Black-necked Stilt, American Avocet breeds rarely, if at all, within the confines of local salt evaporation ponds.

American Avocet was initially confirmed at the Soscol Ferry Road water treatment facility in 1991. One observer discovered three pairs as well as two fledglings on May 26; a fourth pair was present June 8. The birds nested at a shallow fresh-water wetland situated between the facility's settling ponds and buildings. On June 20 one year later, an atlaser located an occupied nest in the Edgerley Island block. Breeding records prior to the Atlas include five egg dates, May 21-June 8, just east of the Napa River at the Slaughterhouse Point lagoon in a non-priority block.

Initial recovery efforts of Napa River floodplain wetlands between Kennedy Park and the Southern Crossing presently attract large numbers of wintering American Avocets. Reclamation of breeding habitat at expanded public lands of the Napa Marsh presents a greater challenge. The recent introduction of permanent water across the alkali flats at Huichica Creek Wildlife Area has created habitat that may prove attractive to American Avocet.

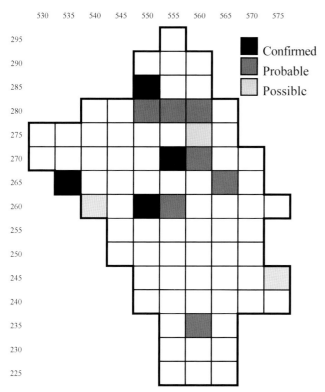

Confirmed
Probable
Possible

Summer resident, rare or absent in winter
Earliest confirmation June 30 – Recently fledged young
Latest confirmation July 11 – Recently fledged young

The Spotted Sandpiper is the lone member of the large global family of birds, Scolopacidae, to nest regularly in Napa County. It is present throughout the year. During winter, it is infrequently found at the larger reservoirs, Berryessa and Hennessey. Such waterside habitat is favored for breeding; the nest is placed along semi-open shores or streambeds where adjacent dense cover is present to shelter the brood. Polyandry is common; females arrive first at the breeding site, defend shoreline, and may mate with several males during a season (Oring *et al.* 1997).

Spotties were found in a total of 14 priority blocks and confirmed in four. Fledglings were seen at the Calistoga water treatment facility on July 5, 1990; on the northwestern shore of Lake Hennessey on June 30, 1991; at upper Putah Creek on July 11, 1991; and at a small reservoir along Hardin Creek on July 5, 1992. July 1992 surveys at Pope and Putah Creeks documented the presence of pairs in several blocks. A pair at Kennedy Park on May 2 was perhaps prevented from breeding when the habitat subsequently dried up. A single pair was believed present in each block where breeding was confirmed.

Spotted Sandpipers were found exclusively at human-created reservoirs and similar impounds. Historically, birds may have nested along the Napa River and the larger interior creeks; however, it is uncertain whether proper habitat ever existed along these streams. Human activity at Lakes Hennessey and Berryessa may limit the breeding success of this unique bird.

FORSTER'S TERN
Sterna forsteri

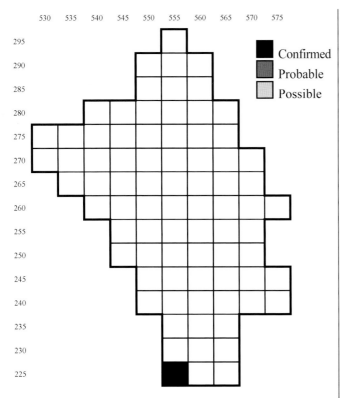

Year-round resident, at times absent in winter
Only confirmation July 1 – Recently fledged young

The lone member of the family Laridae currently known to breed in Napa County, Forster's Tern is a year-round resident of the tidal district. It may be seen foraging almost anywhere over the bay and river, sloughs and salt ponds. Fewer birds are present during winter. Forster's Tern nests colonially on islands and beaches, on sand or among accumulated tidal debris. Nests in the Napa Marsh are commonly on artificial structures.

Forster's Tern was confirmed in a priority block only near Little Island. A trio of atlasers found six downy young being fed by adults on July 1, 1992, on a small sandy island partly covered by concrete rubble. Forster's Tern was also discovered nesting in one non-priority block; the first Napa County breeding records were obtained at Russ Island and Island No. 2 on June 17, 1989 (Bailey *et al.* 1989). An estimated 60 pairs nested atop five duck blinds at the Can Club in that block in 1991. Terns were observed at Lake Berryessa and in three additional tidal blocks May 22- June 23.

Forster's Tern can adapt to habitat change, colonizing suitable sites as they occur (McNicholl *et al.* 2001). Flood and storms frequently alter the Napa Marsh, and Atlas records indicate that human activity plays an additional unintentional role in the creation of nest sites. Perhaps future reclamation efforts in the marsh will purposefully consider the Forster's Tern.

ROCK DOVE
Columba livia

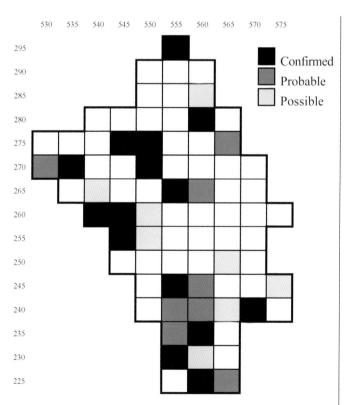

	Confirmed
	Probable
	Possible

Year-round resident
Earliest confirmation March 8 – Occupied nest
Latest confirmation June 23 – Recently fledged young

Probably the most familiar species in the country, the introduced Rock Dove does not hold the attention of birdwatchers for very long. Perhaps it is because their habitat is our own, and we are not altogether pleased with our creation and the creatures attracted to it. Rock Doves place their nests in buildings (a stone house above Soda Canyon) and exotic landscaping (a Carneros Valley palm tree). Nests may be used repeatedly during a year and, over successive years, may attain a mass of over four pounds (Johnson 1992). Nests are preferably concealed deep within a chosen structure, often under conditions of near darkness (Baicich and Harrison 1997).

An occupied nest southeast of Yountville on March 8 precedes five additional reports April 24-June 23. Nest building was observed at Calistoga April 12 and at two Pope Valley locations April 24 and 26. Nestlings were seen in three blocks between April 27 at St. Helena and July 1 at Knoxville. Fledglings in three blocks span June 7-23.

While wild populations may still use ledges and cliffs as breeding sites, observers did not describe such behavior during the Atlas and doves are almost never seen at such sites in Napa County. A pre-Atlas breeding record in 1982 at the old Yountville Crossroad bridge was in as wild a situation as any in the historical record. Rock Dove is strictly a species of the county's cities, towns, and agricultural areas.

BAND-TAILED PIGEON
Columba fasciata

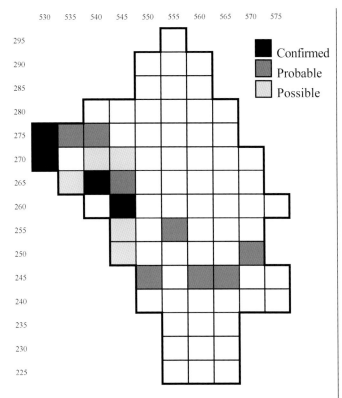

Year-round resident, winter abundance is variable
Earliest confirmation February 1 – Nest with eggs
Latest confirmation July 8 – Recently fledged young

The Band-tailed Pigeon is a resident throughout the Coast Ranges but can be a difficult bird to find during a given year in Napa County. Winter flocks exploit one food source at a time before moving on (Keppie and Braun 2000), and few flocks remain in our area after April. Fruiting madrone is an important food source during winter; breeding birds are primarily found in mixed forests of redwood-Douglas fir, oak, and madrone. Nesting habitat varies among populations in California (Keppie and Braun 2000), and the distribution of Atlas records indicates that fir is preferred over oak in Napa County.

Fledglings were found in the Bothe-Napa Valley SP and Mt. St. Helena blocks on July 1 and 2, 1989, and a nest with eggs was discovered on the mountain's southwestern slope Jan. 30, 1992. Peak nesting is early and mid-summer, but eggs are known in early February in California (Keppie and Braun 2000). Fledglings were also seen near St. Helena on July 8, 1990. All probable data refers to pairs, with five records May 25-June 14 and a pair southeast of Lake Hennessey on April 1. Total reports during Atlas years ranged from ten in 1990 to one in 1993.

Band-tailed Pigeon was shot in large numbers early in the 20th century, prompting a cessation of hunting from 1913-1932. Currently, numbers are not known to be increasing. It remains a game bird in California, but hunting was halted in the 1990s in Washington and Nevada (Keppie and Braun 2000).

MOURNING DOVE
Zenaida macroura

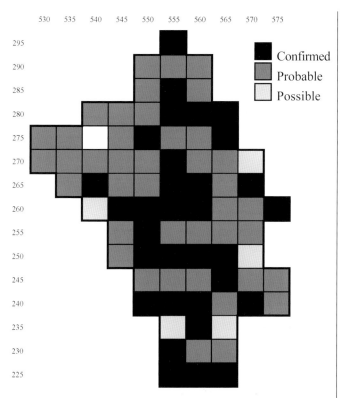

Confirmed
Probable
Possible

Year-round resident
Earliest confirmation April 6 – Occupied nest
Latest confirmation July 10 – Recently fledged young

The Mourning Dove is a common resident throughout Napa County. Its song is a reliable sign of spring in a country where the season can be difficult to define. Doves are successful in a variety of wooded and open habitats: in agricultural areas where belts of trees are present, and in the yard or garden. Humans offer endless opportunities for Mourning Doves to thrive, creating a varied landscape, expanding sources of water, and serving them at feeding stations. California is an important wintering site for migratory doves (Mirarchi & Baskett 1994).

One-half of 170 egg dates in California reported in Bent (1932) fall between early May and mid-June. More than one-half of Atlas confirmations were obtained between May 31-June 25. The five nest building reports span April 16-June 1. Occupied nests were seen between April 10 and June 20. Three egg dates span May 21-June 25; nestlings were found at Bothe and Putah Creek June 18 and 19, respectively. Fledglings were at Chiles Valley May 8, Oakville July 10, and eight additional blocks June 7-18. Mated pairs represent 93 percent of probable reports. Second or third broods after June are not well represented by Atlas data. Historical examples include eggs on July 2 at the Napa River Ecological Reserve and nestlings on July 27 in Jamieson Canyon.

Mourning Doves are an adaptable species. A game bird in California, an estimated 2 million (www.dfg.ca.gov) are taken annually. However, while hunters are diminishing in numbers in California, the Mourning Dove is not.

GREATER ROADRUNNER
Geococcyx californianus

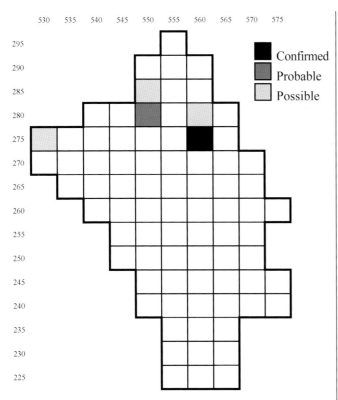

Confirmed
Probable
Possible

Year-round resident
Only confirmation April 30 – Carrying food

The Greater Roadrunner is a terrestrial cuckoo. It may even be found along roads, usually rocky tracks through open chaparral and mixed foothill pine-oak woodland. Sunny openings are important, attracting herptilian food such as fence lizards or invertebrate food in the form of grasshoppers. Roadrunners are also found in more open grassland and at the edges of cultivation. According to Hughes (1996), roadrunner "distribution in northern California is limited to level areas of open ground and tracts of brush and trees."

George Gamble met a roadrunner carrying food for young (a lizard) in the pine-oak woodland near the Boy Scout Camp at Lake Berryessa on April 30, 1993. A mated pair was found in Snell Valley in the spring of 1991. Individuals were seen April 22-June 30 during three different years at Mt. St. Helena, upper Putah Creek, and Eticuera Creek.

The Greater Roadrunner has always been elusive in Napa County; the Atlas confirmation represents the first breeding record. Historical reports are mostly from the Berryessa and Knoxville area. Recent information describes roadrunner as resident at a ranch on Atlas Peak Rd. (R. Leong, pers. comm.) Roadrunner is extirpated from the northern Sacramento Valley and Bay Area (Hughes 1996), and, in the words of Ralph Hoffmann (1927) "will not persist unless some land (is) left, too broken for cultivation, where chaparral still flourishes."

Sponsored by David Takeuchi

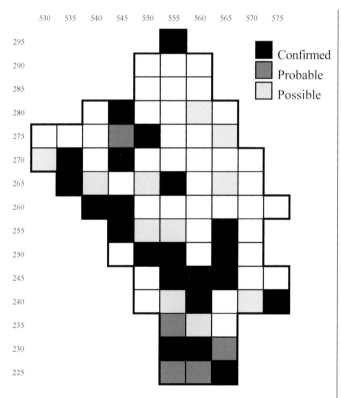

	Confirmed
■	Confirmed
▨	Probable
□	Possible

Year-round resident
Earliest confirmation April 7 – Nest with young
Latest confirmation August 9 – Recently fledged
young

Except for the occasional rasping flight call, the Barn Owl is the most silent of our common owls. Quiet and entirely nocturnal, it is closely associated with human habitation. It hunts over cities and roosts and raises young in ranch sheds, barns, and palm trees. In the Central Valley of California more than half of all Barn Owl Pairs are double-brooded (Marti 1992).

Atlasers found nine nests with young: April 7 in Napa and four nests in both May and June, the last of which was southwest of Napa on June 30. Fledglings were found in 11 blocks, including April 13 at Gordon Valley, five between May 15 and June 22, and five July 15-August 9. Seventy-three percent of Atlas confirmations came from blocks that are primarily urban or agricultural. The five probable records represent either territorial birds or pairs; except for a Pope Valley territory, all were agricultural blocks at the edges of the city of Napa.

Barn Owls favor the most settled parts of the county – the Napa Valley and the city of Napa. The interior valleys also support a number of breeding pairs. Upland forests and chaparral are avoided. Up the Valley, agricultural land with a diverse population of rodents is important to maintaining Barn Owl populations (Marti 1992). The presence of nest sites is equally important, and a program called "Habitat for Hooters," which places artificial structures in viticultural habitat, may succeed in increasing the population.

Sponsored by William and Doris Proctor

WESTERN SCREECH-OWL
Otus kennicottii

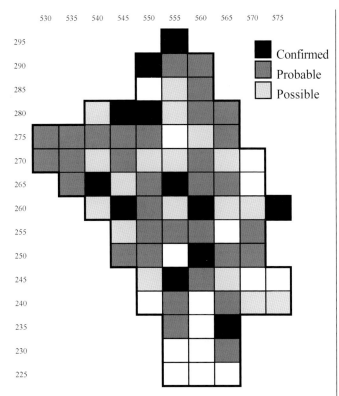

Confirmed
Probable
Possible

Year-round resident
Earliest confirmation March 13 – Occupied nest
Latest confirmation July 12 – Recently fledged young

A few ambitious atlasers conducting extensive surveys during late winter and early spring determined that Western Screech-Owl is the most common owl in Napa County. Screech-owls were found in a variety of wooded habitats, perhaps preferring oaks and avoiding dense closed-canopy forests. Screech-owls nest primarily in natural tree cavities, and old woodpecker holes are particularly important. Artificial nest boxes are used for both nesting and roosting.

Screech-owls were heard calling in 15 blocks between February 5 and April 8. Adults were observed defending territory in ten blocks, primarily during March surveys specifically directed at finding owls. Territorial singing males were heard through April 30, and nine of 13 reports of mated pairs were obtained before April 2. A nest was occupied in Soda Canyon on March 13. Nests with young were found in four blocks from May 25 southwest of Knoxville through June 26 south of Yountville. Fledglings were discovered in six blocks between June 4 at St. Helena and July 12 near Monticello Dam. Except for higher numbers in adjacent blocks along Trout Creek Ridge, abundance estimates were between 1-10 pairs per block.

In Napa County, the Western Screech-Owl is probably truly absent only from the urban habitat of the city of Napa and the pasture and tidal country of the south. Suitable breeding habitat exists in each of the interior blocks where owls were not found. Given sufficient time and good survey conditions, atlasers might well have found birds in each of those interior blocks.

Sponsored by William Provan

GREAT HORNED OWL
Bubo virginianus

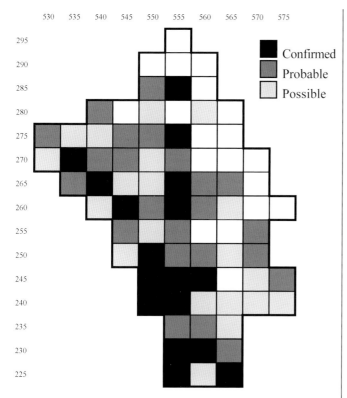

Confirmed
Probable
Possible

Year-round resident
Earliest confirmation February 14 – Recently fledged young
Latest confirmation August 3 – Recently fledged young

The Great Horned Owl is described as having a "wider range of nest sites than any other bird in the Americas" (Houston *et al.* 1998). Skinner (1938) found it difficult to determine any site preference, "and, if so, for what." We don't know a great deal about nest placement in Napa County, but we do know that this big owl fits itself into almost any habitat. It hunts over tidal marsh, residential streets, vineyards, redwood canyons, and broken chaparral. Its nest is often formerly one of a hawk or crow; however, an unadorned, moss-covered recess in a valley oak frequently shelters the female and her clutch.

Atlas data reflects the Great Horned Owl's lengthy breeding season. Pairs and territorial individuals were widespread by Valentine's Day, continuing into early April. An occupied nest was discovered at Bothe on March 3. Nests with young were found along Atlas Peak Road on April 15 and at Carneros on June 30. Fledglings were seen during a nearly six-month period and represented 84 percent of all confirmations. Fledglings were first detected in the hills west of Yountville on March 17 and last in northwest Napa on August 3.

The majority of Great Horned Owl confirmations came from urban edges and densely settled rural areas. Confirming evidence is more difficult to obtain in remote regions owing to time constraints of atlasers combined with the owl's nocturnal habits. Habitat restrictions do, however, indicate a real absence from oak savannah and hard chaparral across a broad area of the northeast.

NORTHERN PYGMY-OWL
Glaucidium gnoma

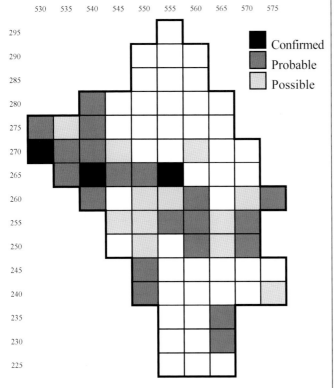

Confirmed
Probable
Possible

Year-round resident
Earliest confirmation June 7 – Recently fledged young
Latest confirmation July 6 – Recently fledged young

As the morning sun moves down an open oak canyon, it may reach the smoldering yellow eyes of a Northern Pygmy-Owl, setting them alight. Northern Pygmy-Owl is our smallest forest owl and the only one active during daylight. These owls are found in a variety of forest edge and interior settings, including Douglas fir-madrone and oak-chaparral. They appear to prefer areas where habitats meet or break up, such as where fir gives way to oak on a north slope or in canyons where oak and bay fade into rock outcrops and stunted trees. This owl species sings the year round and perhaps never hunts in darkness (Holt and Petersen 2000).

Reports of singing and territorial birds and mated pairs were obtained in nine blocks during March. Birds continued to sing through July 4 at Lake Marie. The last of eight records of territorial behavior was at Table Mt. on July 1. Mated pairs were seen at four locations, lastly on July 27 along the Palisades. Breeding was confirmed when fledglings were discovered northwest of Calistoga on June 7, at Bothe on June 18, and on the slopes of Chiles Valley on July 6. One-half of reports from 14 blocks judged abundance at a single pair, while an experienced owler surveying Trout Creek Ridge at Lake Berryessa estimated the presence of 11-100 pairs.

Northern Pygmy-Owls often nest in cavities created by Hairy Woodpeckers (R. Leong, pers. comm.). Not coincidentally, the Atlas revealed that the distribution of both that woodpecker and this owl are very similar.

Sponsored by Robin Leong

BURROWING OWL
Athene cunicularia

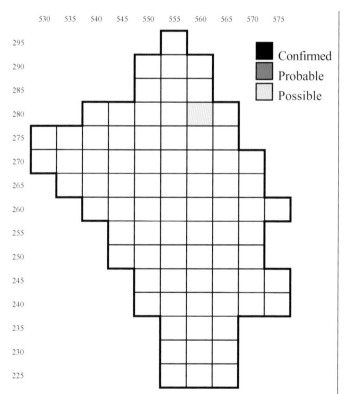

■ Confirmed
▨ Probable
☐ Possible

Formerly year-round resident, possibly extirpated as a breeding species
Only possible May 10 – Species in habitat

Finding a Burrowing Owl in Napa County has long been a task requiring patience. A wintering bird is occasionally present and will stay in a small area for weeks or a couple of months. But summer observations are few. Burrowing Owl is found in rolling or level grassland, especially where ground squirrel burrows provide shelter for the roost or nest. Nest site fidelity is believed high (Trulio 1995). Over the past few decades, Burrowing Owl reports have been concentrated at Lake Berryessa and along the upland margins of the southern tidal marshes.

A Burrowing Owl at the north end of Lake Berryessa on May 10, 1990, is the only report of a possible breeding bird. An owl observed east of Rutherford May 1, 1990, was not in breeding habitat. Two breeding records precede the Atlas: a 1938 nest at Buchli Station, and fledglings at the western end of American Canyon Road July 15, 1962. Past breeding may have also occurred at Berryessa.

The historic distribution of Burrowing Owl in Napa County is uncertain. Most recently, owls were seen at Alston Park and Huichica Creek Wildlife Area in the late 1990s but have been seen only at Huichica in the 21st century. Development and intensive agricultural practices continue to cause serious population declines in Central California. DeSante *et al.* (1991) believe that approximately two-thirds of breeding locations and breeding pairs in the Central Valley and San Francisco Bay Area may have been lost between 1981-1991. Burrowing Owl is a Species of Special Concern in California.

Sponsored by Jo Maillard

SPOTTED OWL
Strix occidentalis

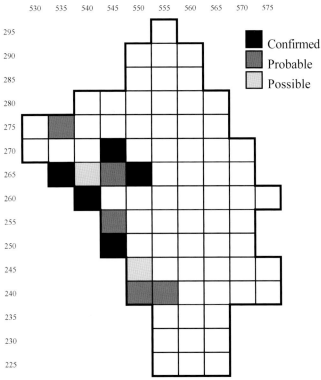

530 535 540 545 550 555 560 565 570 575

■	Confirmed
▨	Probable
▢	Possible

Year-round resident
Earliest confirmation April 8 – Occupied nest
Latest confirmation July 30 – Feeding young

The Northern Spotted Owl, S.o. caurina, inhabits about 25 breeding territories in Napa County scattered throughout the mixed forests and canyons of the western hills and Angwin. It was first identified as a local resident in the early 1960s, and extensive surveys after 1989 fully documented its distribution. Northern Spotted Owl is very territorial in Napa County, with pairs spaced no closer than one mile. Nesting and roosting sites are in forests with at least 85 percent canopy closure. Many Northern Spotted Owls in Napa County also probably forage in brushy areas adjacent to forests, where the Dusky-footed Woodrat comprises 75 percent of their prey.

Atlas data includes occupied nests at Howell Mt. April 8, 1992, and Ink Grade May 16, 1993. A nest with young was discovered at Bothe May 26, 1989; fledglings were near Dry Creek July 1, 1990, and Spring Mt. July 30, 1989. Mated pairs were detected in four blocks March 10-August 4. Historical records describe a breeding season from March 29 (occupied nest) to July 30 (fledged young).

The four Northern Spotted Owl territories in the Angwin area were no longer occupied by 2002. Accelerated urbanization, viticulture, and fire have resulted in forest fragmentation and the owl's displacement. Proliferation of agriculture in the west could result in losses unless size and spacing of such activities is designed to insure sufficient nesting, roosting, and foraging habitat for known territories. The Northern Spotted Owl, *S.o. caurina,* is Federally Threatened throughout its range.
—*Ted Wooster and Murray Berner*

Sponsored by Ted Wooster

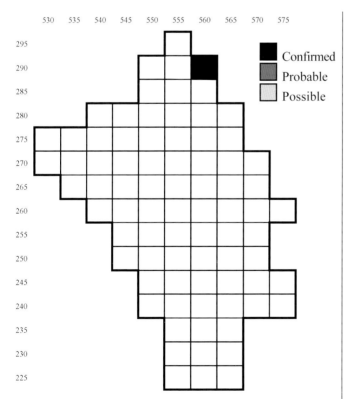

530 535 540 545 550 555 560 565 570 575

295 290 285 280 275 270 265 260 255 250 245 240 235 230 225

■ Confirmed
▨ Probable
▢ Possible

Rare, possibly a year-round resident, status poorly understood

Only confirmation June 23 – Recently fledged young

The Long-eared Owl hunts at night, roosts in dense vegetation during the day, and is our least common upland owl. It was found in a single Atlas block. It hunts over open terrain, nesting in adjacent dense cover. Riparian corridors and belts of trees in open country are typical, as are thickly vegetated lower parts of drainages in dry upland environments (Grinnell and Miller 1944, Marks *et al.* 1994).

On June 23, 1990, several days after George Gamble flushed a Long-eared Owl in a canyon at his Lake Berryessa ranch, Bill Grummer visited the site in search of breeding evidence. With patience, he was eventually able to see three owls simultaneously, including fledglings. The nesting canyon extended north-south, with blue oak woodland to the east, chaparral on the west. The canyon bottom held pools of water and a 100-foot wide strip of live oak, buckeye, and bay. In 1991 an active Cooper's Hawk nest was found at this site, which may have significance for the owl: long-eared commonly raises young in the old stick nests of other species (Marks *et al.* 1994).

The Atlas record represents the first and only breeding record of Long-eared Owl in Napa County. Mr. Gamble also observed owls in this canyon prior to the Atlas. An owl in Redwood Canyon in May 1981 and at least two in the Yountville Hills during January 1982 and 1983 may represent the only other county records. Due primarily to vanishing grassland and riparian habitat, Long-eared Owl is a Species of Special Concern in California.

SHORT-EARED OWL
Asio flammeus

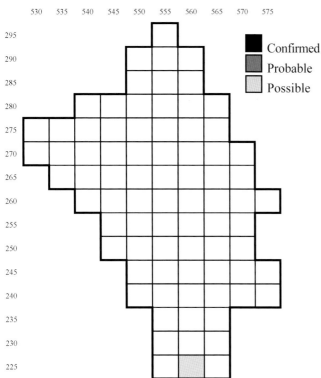

Confirmed
Probable
Possible

Winter resident, occasionally present in summer
Only possible June 2 – Species in habitat

On occasion during winter, one or two foraging Short-eared Owls may appear at dusk or dawn at favored grassland margins of the Napa Marsh. The owls respond to cyclic populations of microtine rodents, and birds are apparently not present every year. However, the number of people actively seeking short-eareds is limited, and the species may often be overlooked. Their conspicuous courtship flight might make them easier to find in the spring; however, there are few county records after March. The observation of a single bird in the Fagan Slough area on June 2, 1989, is the only Atlas record. Fagan Slough and adjacent airport grassland have commonly supported wintering owls.

There are no breeding records in Napa County. The possibility grows smaller each year as habitat is lost at the edges of the Napa Marsh. Development around the airport and in American Canyon continues to constrict foraging habitat. Short-eared Owls at Huichica Creek Wildlife Area in recent winters may be impacted by the increased presence of non-hunting humans with free-running dogs. Breeding status aside, their continued presence in winter is at risk. Short-eared Owl is presently a Species of Special Concern in California.

NORTHERN SAW-WHET OWL
Aegolius acadicus

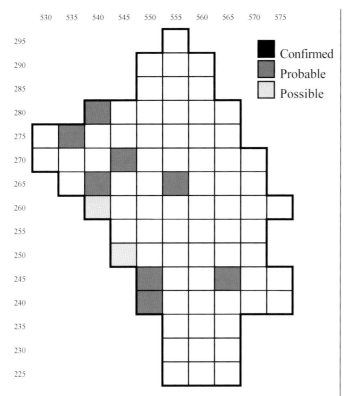

- Confirmed
- Probable
- Possible

Year-round resident
Earliest probable February 22 – Multiple observations
at same location
Latest probable July 6 – Pair observed

Completely nocturnal in its activities, the Northern Saw-whet Owl is Napa's uncommon, small upland owl. Preferring forests where conifers are present, its habitat overlaps that of the Northern Pygmy-Owl; however, it is generally found at lower elevations (Cannings 1993). Saw-whet inhabits ponderosa pine forest in the far northwest, using redwood and fir canyons in uplands elsewhere. It will use nest boxes (Cannings 1993).

Saw-whet Owls were discovered in ten priority blocks. Ninety percent of records were obtained before April 10, representing either singing or territorial owls. They were heard as early as New Year's Day west of St. Helena and through March 20 in the Redwood Canyon area. Four of the ten records span a ten-day period beginning March 16. Two more easterly interior records include a calling bird in the Milliken area through February 22.

Atlas data likely reflects the genuine rarity of the saw-whet as a breeding species. Historical records are two: nests with young at Wall Rd. May 14, 1985, and Ritchey Canyon May 22, 1988. Maintaining the small population of this owl depends on the conservation of other species as well. The abandoned cavities of Pileated Woodpecker and Northern Flicker are important nest sites for Northern Saw-whet Owl (Grummer *et al.* 1990). The owl and the woodpeckers therefore depend upon the integrity of existing mature forests.

COMMON POORWILL
Phalaenoptilus nuttallii

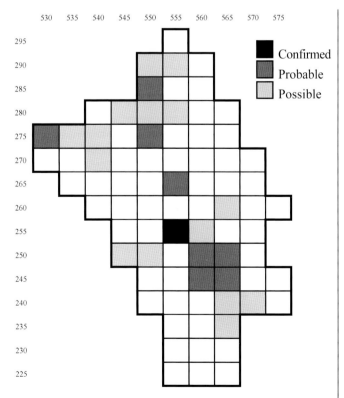

Summer resident, winter status poorly understood
Only confirmation September 3 – Nest with young

Known by Native Americans as the "Sleeping One" from its strategy of entering a state of torpor during winter, the Common Poorwill has been found "asleep" during January in Napa County at the Palisades. The poorwill is a bird of rough chaparral slopes, bouldery outcrops, and rocky tableland. It is most often located by voice but may be seen at night foraging from mountain roads. Poorwill is often double-brooded, and the breeding season extends from March into September (Baicich and Harrison 1997).

Atlas records of Common Poorwill span nearly six months. A singing male northwest of Pope Valley on March 6 initiated the season, and it concluded with the lone confirmation of the Atlas period, a September 3, 1989, nest with young discovered southeast of Lake Hennessey. There is little pattern to be gleaned from the 23 possible and probable records. Eight are July records, largely due to the efforts of two atlasers working to find birds in the Milliken and Palisades regions. Poorwill was perhaps one of the most difficult species on which to gather data. Its nocturnal habits and often daunting habitat proved a difficult challenge.

The range of Common Poorwill encompasses two distinct regions: a narrow stretch of foothills from Lake Hennessey southeast to Wild Horse Valley, and a band along the entire northwestern border of the county. Two blocks on the southern slopes of Mt. St. John provided the only records west of the Napa Valley.

WHITE-THROATED SWIFT
Aeronautes saxatalis

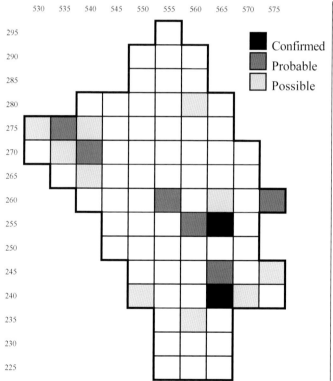

Confirmed
Probable
Possible

Year-round resident
Earliest confirmation May 13 – Feeding young
Latest confirmation June 23 – Occupied nest

The White-throated Swift is an amazing bird that flies in spectacular places. Often beyond visual detection over ridges and canyons, it sends its skittering calls dwindling down to earth from an empty sky. The swifts come to earth to nest in fissures in cliffs overlooking canyons and valleys. Human structures present nesting opportunities; swifts nested on the Southern Crossing bridge in 1986 and 1987.

On June 23, 1990, an occupied nest was found in a rock outcrop overlooking Sarco Creek; and on May 13, 1990, adults were feeding fledglings above Capell Valley. Bent (1940) describes California's early egg date as May 8. However, more recent evidence during April includes fledglings in the Mojave Desert (Ryan and Collins 2000) and an occupied nest in Monterey County (Roberson and Tenney 1993). A Southern Crossing nest held young on May 20. Probable reports include pairs in four blocks April 13-May 16 and a swift entering a probable nest site at Milliken Canyon April 8, 1991. In addition to Milliken, all probable records are from traditionally occupied areas, including Monticello Dam, Rector Canyon, and the Palisades. Possible reports are concentrated in blocks adjacent to those areas. Swifts have a "great cruising radius" (Grinnell and Miller 1944) and can appear overhead anytime or anywhere.

White-throated Swifts are most readily seen at the Palisades, Mt. St. Helena, and Monticello Dam. On chilly spring mornings at the Palisades, swifts fly close against the stone walls, where their voices echo and one may marvel at their speed.

BLACK-CHINNED HUMMINGBIRD
Archilochus alexandri

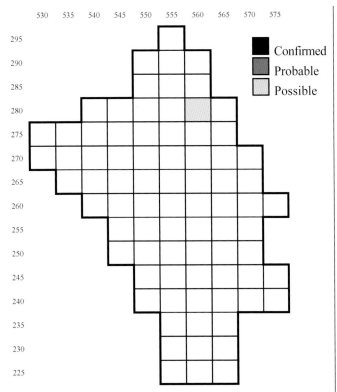

Confirmed
Probable
Possible

Rare visitor, late spring/early summer
Only possible May 1 – Species in habitat

North of the San Francisco Bay, the Black-chinned Hummingbird is found exclusively east of the coastal fog belt. Females nest in deciduous trees in canyons and stream bottoms. The males summer higher up the canyon sides once their fertilization duty is complete, amid live oak and chaparral (Grinnell and Miller 1944). The lone Atlas record, at the northwestern part of Lake Berryessa, is well beyond the usual summer fog, and the canyon habitat is typical of the species south of San Francisco Bay and in the Sierra foothills. However, George Gamble's May 1, 1990, observation of a single Black-chinned Hummingbird represents one of only about four records of the species in Napa County. Details of date and locale of one of the previous records are known: one bird at Cleary Reserve on May 11, 1976.

Black-chinned Hummingbird occurs regularly in adjacent Yolo County and at Liberty Island in Solano Co. It has been seen occasionally near the Napa Co. line in the Vaca Mountains at Gates and Mix Canyons. The black-chin may yet be discovered breeding on the Napa side of those remote county line ridges.

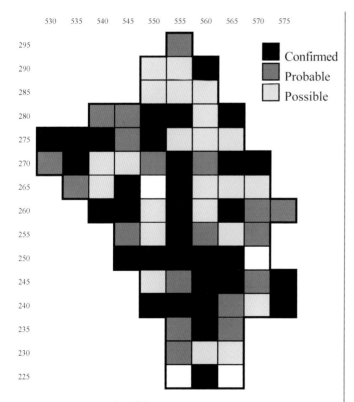

Confirmed
Probable
Possible

Year-round resident
Earliest confirmation February 22 – Carrying nesting material
Latest confirmation August 7 – Recently fledged young

The nesting season of Anna's Hummingbird is perhaps counterintuitive to human perception of a fragile hummer that depends upon the warmth and blossoms of spring. Instead, the season begins with winter rains as males defend slopes of blossoming chaparral and females start their nests, usually in nearby oak woodland. The season extends into the summer, when flowers are few and competition with other hummingbirds, including young of the year, is greatest. Introduced flowering vegetation has apparently not affected the timing of the breeding season (Russell 1996).

Each of the types of confirming behavior extended over long intervals during the Atlas period. Nest construction was found from Feb. 22 through June 13. Females were on nests by Mar. 15 through June 16. Nestlings appeared from Mar. 30 to June 15. Fledglings were seen as early as Apr. 14 and as late as Aug. 7. Reports of courtship or territorial display in 11 blocks span Mar. 27-June 22. Since atlasers were in the field primarily between April and July, data is limited from the earliest part of the nesting season. Historical records include nest building Feb. 15-22 and nestlings Feb. 15 and 25.

Anna's Hummingbird is found throughout the county in its traditional habitat and has benefited from feeders and exotic vegetation, expanding its distribution. Once a California endemic, on a larger scale Anna's Hummingbird has spread north to Canada (Russell 1996), and, in smaller, local terms, into everyone's backyard with a bottlebrush or a feeder.

ALLEN'S HUMMINGBIRD
Selasphorus sasin

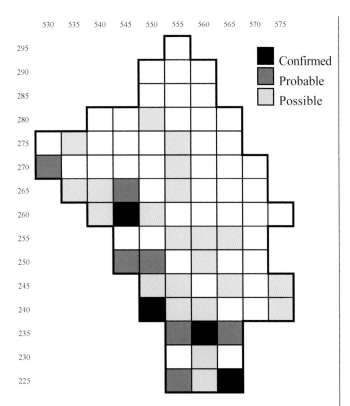

530 535 540 545 550 555 560 565 570 575

295
290
285
280
275
270
265
260
255
250
245
240
235
230
225

■ Confirmed
▨ Probable
□ Possible

Late winter/summer resident
Earliest confirmation March 1 – Nest building
Latest confirmation April 29 – Recently fledged young

Perhaps the best place to catch sight of Allen's Hummingbird as it arrives during February is a eucalyptus grove in full flower in the far south of the county. Many remain to nest, but fortunately they also move up the Napa Valley into riparian groves and into cool canyons on either side of the Valley. For all the competition associated with hummingbirds at feeders, Allen's is remarkable in that several females will nest in close proximity (Bent 1940, Mitchell 2000).

The four confirmations are representative of the species' early nesting season: nest building in Napa on March 1; eggs in Jamieson Canyon March 17; fledglings on April 20 and 29 at St. Helena and Redwood Canyon, respectively. Probable records of paired birds spanned March 5-June 2. Observations of the male's spectacular "pendulum" display may be inferred by courtship records in the tidal district April 7 and on the slopes of Mt. St. John May 14. Allen's Hummingbird commonly raises two broods (Baicich and Harrison 1997, Mitchell 2000); therefore, the handful of late June observations may represent nesting birds. There is a July 15, 1941, record of fledglings at Howell Mt. The few early season confirmations probably reflect the limited fieldwork carried out during March and April when hummers are already actively raising young.

Allen's Hummingbird is believed largely bound within the inland reach of summer fog during the nesting season (Mitchell 2000). The complete lack of strong evidence of breeding east of the Valley, and, therefore, beyond the fog, supports that belief.

Sponsored by John Galloway and Cecilia Lee

BELTED KINGFISHER
Ceryle alcyon

ZL

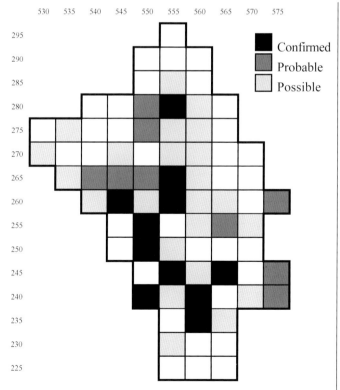

Confirmed
Probable
Possible

Year-round resident
Earliest confirmation May 8 – Carrying food
Latest confirmation July 18 – Feeding young

The Belted Kingfisher is found wherever the water runs clear and fish venture near the surface. During the breeding season, lakes and streams often must provide a deep vertical bank in which the kingfisher digs a nest chamber. However, nests are also excavated in gravel pits, road cuts, or similar earthen banks - often far from water. Kingfisher territories are larger on rivers than on lakes, and smaller lakes are favored over larger; territories shrink when prey density is high and expand when it is low (Davis 1982, Salyer and Legler 1946).

Two nests were discovered during the Atlas, both on the Napa River at the city of Napa. Nestlings were found in the south Napa block on May 20, 1991, and, to the north, an occupied nest was described on May 24, 1990. The three records of adults carrying food span May 8-June 18. Fledglings were observed in six blocks, June 4-July 18. Probable data refers exclusively to pairs, March 25-June 20.

The Napa River corridor provided six Atlas confirmations and almost one-third of all Atlas records. Kingfishers also nested at Chiles Valley, Redwood Creek, and Milliken Creek. Lake Hennessey and perhaps the Putah Creek arm of Lake Berryessa were the lone lake nesting records. At county lakes, high surface water temperatures reduce food available to adults feeding young, and human disturbance may preclude nesting altogether. Along every valley stream, the maintenance of water quality, sufficient stream flow, and nest sites are vital to the county population.

ACORN WOODPECKER
Melanerpes formicivorus

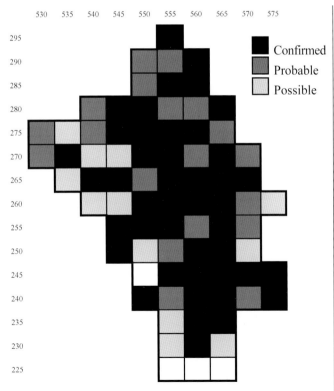

	Confirmed
(black)	Confirmed
(gray)	Probable
(light)	Possible

Year-round resident
Earliest confirmation April 15 – Occupied nest
Latest confirmation July 27 – Occupied nest

In a family of birds known for their discreet behavior during the nesting season, Acorn Woodpeckers are a bit loose. Wild plumage, a laughing voice, and large families betray them at all seasons. Colonies are established in oak woodland, from sea level at Kennedy Park to near 3000' at the Palisades. Dead trees and snags where acorns are stored and defended in "granaries" are essential in their habitat. Much of our detailed knowledge of breeding Acorn Woodpeckers in California comes from research at Carmel Valley's Hastings Reservation, where the egg-laying peak extends from late April through late June (Koenig *et al.* 1995).

Eleven occupied nests found during the Atlas study spanned April 15-May 16, and five June 17-July 27. Nestlings were discovered in six blocks between May 13 at Conn Valley and July 1 at Pope Valley. Adults carried food for young April 30-July 2. Fledglings were seen at 13 locations, from May 9 near Turner Mt. through July 18 at Lake Berryessa. During years of poor early reproduction combined with bountiful acorns, a late breeding season may be initiated, with eggs in August or September (Koenig *et al.* 1995).

Acorn Woodpeckers depend on the health and integrity of oak woodland. Development, firewood cutting, poor regeneration, and Sudden Oak Death threaten both oaks and the woodpecker habitat. Snags for granaries are especially important at the urban edge (Koenig *et al.* 1995). Atlas abundance estimates were quite high throughout the county; however, many colonies of Acorn Woodpecker are not secure.

Sponsored by Ted and Rochella Wooster

NUTTALL'S WOODPECKER
Picoides nuttallii

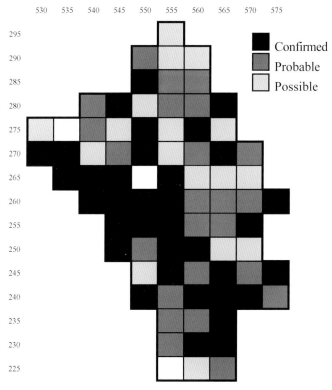

Confirmed
Probable
Possible

Year-round resident
Earliest confirmation April 4 – Carrying food
Latest confirmation July 14 – Carrying food

Nuttall's Woodpecker inhabits oak associations throughout Napa County, including savannah, riparian, chaparral, madrone, and Douglas fir. Nuttall's is usually less vocal around the nest than the Acorn Woodpecker, its more conspicuous fellow oak specialist, yet was confirmed in 46 percent of the 76 Atlas blocks where it was found.

An early nest was occupied near Bothe April 5. Nestlings were found at Yountville April 7 and in three additional blocks May 19-June 15. Adults carried food for young at Pope Valley April 4, at Milliken July 14, and in ten blocks between May 2 and 16. Fledglings were seen during mid-May in two blocks and in ten blocks June 7-July 11. The incubation period of Nuttall's Woodpecker is 14 days (Winkler *et al.* 1995). Counting back from the April 4 Pope Valley and the April 7 Yountville records would produce egg dates that precede and equal, respectively, the March 25 early California date reported in Lowther (2000). California's latest known egg date is June 14 (Bent 1939); therefore, the four July confirmations fall within the known limits of the species' nesting season. Probable reports describe territorial defense and mated or courting pairs March 25-July 20.

The range of Nuttall's Woodpecker in the county closely follows the distribution of oaks. Nuttall's is less common or absent at the higher elevations of Mt. St. Helena and the Palisades. It is also more locally distributed across the extensive areas of hard chaparral in the northeastern quarter of the county.

DOWNY WOODPECKER
Picoides pubescens

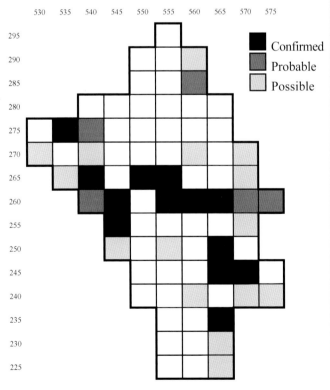

- Confirmed
- Probable
- Possible

Year-round resident
Earliest confirmation April 11 – Carrying food
Latest confirmation July 9 – Feeding young

The Downy Woodpecker is our smallest and quietest resident in the woodpecker family and perhaps the least common; many days may pass between encounters. Downies frequent streams and other lowland areas where permanent moisture allows willow and other softwoods to grow. A few are found at the mouths of canyons among alders, and they will stray into upland hardwoods at any time during the year.

Bent (1939) reports eggs in California April 7-June 9; therefore, an adult carrying food for young in the Circle Oaks block on April 11 is unusual. Records on May 21 and June 1 are more typical. The lone report of a nest with young came from the lower Chiles Valley on May 24. Nine records of fledglings commence June 1 at lower Capell Creek, extending through July 9 at St. Helena; six of these records were obtained after June 30. Possible and probable data refers to individuals and pairs during May and June. Fifteen of the 17 blocks estimating abundance reported ten or fewer pairs.

Downy Woodpecker was found in many of the county's lowland valleys, including Napa, Chiles, Capell, and Wooden. Its absence from Pope and Conn Valley is surprising. While there are anecdotal reports of downies breeding in the Napa Valley south of Rutherford, atlasers did not find confirming evidence. The area contains an abundance of smaller streams in addition to the river; however, the fragmented nature of the habitat may deter Downy Woodpecker from breeding.

HAIRY WOODPECKER
Picoides villosus

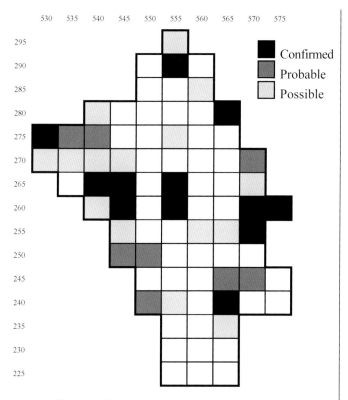

Year-round resident
Earliest confirmation April 10 – Occupied nest
Latest confirmation July 25 – Feeding young

Hairy Woodpecker is the resident white-backed wood-pecker of Napa's wooded foothills. Territories are large, and it is an uncommon species inhabiting relatively densely forested areas where large trees are present, especially associations of Douglas fir and coast redwood. It occurs primarily in the western hills and in higher elevation forests of Howell Mt. and Mt. St. Helena. A few are found in the eastern canyons and at foothill-pine-dominated arid interior sites. Hairy Woodpecker usually excavates its nest hole in a decaying part of a living tree (Winkler *et al.* 1995).

Hairy Woodpeckers occupied nests at Bothe April 10 and at upper Chiles Creek June 17. Adults carried food for young in five blocks May 14-25. Fledglings were reported at four locations May 29-June 14 and at St. Helena July 25. Additional records include birds entering probable nest cavities May 7 and 25 near Wooden Valley and Swartz Canyon, respectively. Abundance estimates were low; higher numbers at Bothe reflect extensive Hairy Woodpecker habitat there.

Evidence suggests that Hairy Woodpecker quickly takes advantage of forests impacted by disease and fire. Bent (1939) describes concentrations at insect-infested Ponderosa pine in northeastern California. After the 1980 Atlas Peak fire, each Napa County woodpecker species appeared in large numbers in the Rector Canyon area, foraging on the killed and decaying foothill pines. Hairy Woodpecker was first noted there during winter 1981-82, and a peak count of 11 birds was made in January 1983. By 1987, Hairy Woodpecker was again absent from Rector.

NORTHERN FLICKER
Colaptes auratus

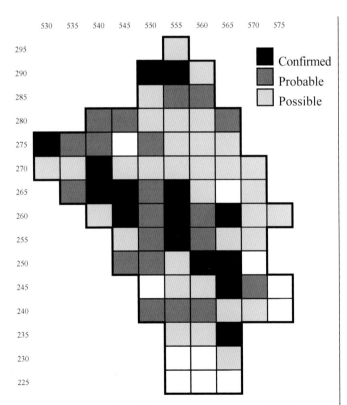

- Confirmed
- Probable
- Possible

Year-round resident, more numerous and widespread in winter
Earliest confirmation April 11 – Occupied nest
Latest confirmation June 25 – Recently fledged young

The Northern Flicker is a ubiquitous presence in a variety of habitats in the county during the winter, but for the breeding season it retires to the forested hills. Napa's flickers appear to favor blue and black oak woodland at middle elevations as well as ponderosa pine wherever it occurs. Nests on the Napa Valley floor are rare. Closed canopy, contiguous forests are generally avoided; flickers require edges and open areas where they can forage on the ground. The birds themselves excavate a nest cavity in dead or partly dead trees. The relatively large cavities are subsequently used as roosting and breeding sites by several bird and mammal species.

Flickers were observed excavating cavities on May 2 near Oakville and May 28 at Eticuera Creek. Occupied nests were found in five blocks between April 11 and June 6. Nests with young were discovered at Spencer Creek on June 19 and in the Milliken Canyon area on June 22. Fledglings were reported in five blocks June 9-25. Possible and probable records account for 46 and 28 percent of the data, respectively. Almost 60 percent of those records are after April and are assumed to be potential breeding birds rather than migrants.

While Atlas data indicates that Northern Flickers are found during the breeding season throughout the county, stronger confirming evidence trends along a relatively narrow, two-block-wide corridor comprising the length of the Napa Valley's eastern hills. This corridor is dominated by a variety of broken pine, oak, and fir forests.

Sponsored by Tom and Jane Blaisdell

PILEATED WOODPECKER
Dryocopus pileatus

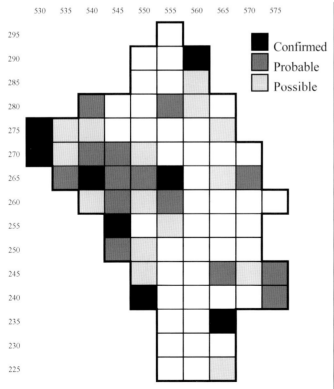

■ Confirmed
■ Probable
□ Possible

Year-round resident
Earliest confirmation April 26 – Occupied nest
Latest confirmation July 15 – Recently fledged young

The Pileated Woodpecker takes up a lot of space. It is the largest woodpecker in the USA, and each pair requires a territory of roughly 400-540 acres, which is defended throughout the year (Bull & Jackson 1995). It is most successful in mature, unbroken, closed canopy, mixed upland forests where large trees provide foraging opportunities and nest sites. Pileateds in the county are also found in more open deciduous forests, where they nest in canyons with extensive stands of mature alder. On occasion individuals have wintered among valley oak at the Napa River Ecological Reserve.

Pileated Woodpeckers occupied nests southwest of St. Helena April 26 and northwest of Calistoga May 1. Nestlings were discovered at Bothe on June 3. Four records of adults with fledglings or young just out of the nest span June 11-30: Mt. St. Helena, upper Eticuera Creek, Los Posadas, and Spencer Creek. Fledglings were seen near Redwood Canyon on the approximate date of July 15. Seventy-one percent of probable records describe mated pairs; potential nest excavation was observed near Angwin May 16. Abundance estimates did not exceed 10 pairs in any block.

The heart of Napa County's Pileated Woodpecker range is the cooler, low-to-middle-elevation forests and canyons from Lokoya to Angwin and Mt. St. Helena. Each of the woodpecker species breeding in these forests creates innumerable tree cavities that benefit small forest owls, mammals, reptiles, and amphibians. This remarkable interdependence of animals is sustained only by the forest's integrity.

Sponsored by Duane and Ann Smith

OLIVE-SIDED FLYCATCHER
Contopus cooperi

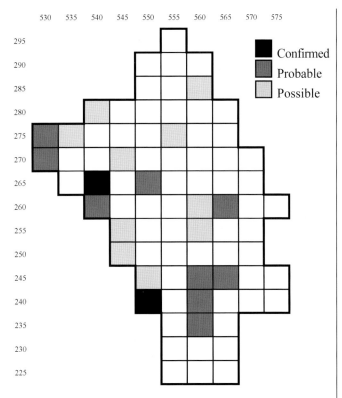

Summer resident
Earliest confirmation June 14 – Carrying food
Latest confirmation July 12 – Feeding young

The Olive-sided Flycatcher winters in northwestern South America. It usually arrives in Napa County after April 20, and migrants are regularly detected through the first half of May. Summer residents favor Douglas fir, especially in open canyons and at forest edges. In parts of the Bay Area, it breeds in eucalyptus groves (Shuford 1993). Among fir specialists, Olive-sided Flycatchers are unique in their preference for such edge habitats (Altman and Sallabanks 2000). In North America their mean egg-laying date of June 22 is among the latest of all Tyrranids, and the five-week interval from egg to fledgling is the longest of any passerine species (Altman and Sallabanks 2000).

There were two Atlas confirmations in 1990: an adult was carrying food at Redwood Canyon on June 14, and adults with fledglings were at Bothe on July 12. Territorial singing males were heard in seven blocks between May 5 near Napa and June 21 at Capell Creek. Seven reports of singing males found on one day only fall between April 28-July 4.

Olive-sided Flycatcher is relatively common locally only at Mt. St. Helena, Bothe, and Redwood Canyon. Elsewhere, atlasers frequently reported only one breeding pair per block. Breeding Bird Survey data since 1966 shows a significant annual decline in the California foothills. Reasons for the decline are complex, but may include the species' naturally low reproductive rate combined with reduced survivorship on deforested tropical American wintering grounds (Altman and Sallabanks 2000). It is a Species of Special Concern in California.

WESTERN WOOD-PEWEE
Contopus sordidulus

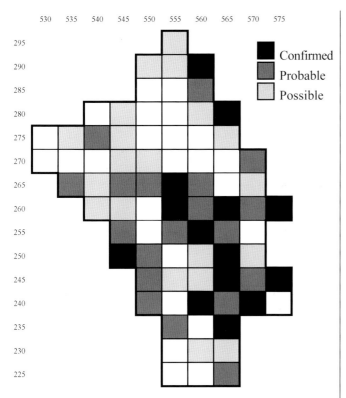

Confirmed
Probable
Possible

Summer resident
Earliest confirmation April 20 – Nest building
Latest confirmation July 15 – Carrying food

The Western Wood-Pewee is a relatively late-arriving migrant, establishing itself in the county at the end of April. Napa's pewees are found primarily in oak woodland, often at isolated outcrops of blue oak in open savannah or in groves of black oak confined to north slopes within chaparral. They are also found in riparian woodland where valley oaks remain and in foothill pine in open oak-chaparral.

Busy upon its arrival, a wood-pewee was building a nest near Monticello Dam on April 20. Adults were carrying food for young at five locations between May 15 at northeastern Lake Berryessa and July 15 at Lake Curry. Nests with young were discovered on the slopes of Mt. St. John June 22 and at Soda Canyon on July 3. Fledglings were seen in four blocks June 9-June 25. Mated pairs and singing males throughout May and June represent probable data. Abundance was low; 18 of 21 reporting blocks estimated ten or fewer pairs.

Grinnell and Miller (1944) describe Western Wood-Pewee as "more widely numerous than any other of our tyrannids." Breeding Bird Survey data shows a 1.5% yearly decline, 1966-99, throughout the American range (Pardieck and Sauer 2000). Significant decline is noted in California, and pewees are among 57 species "most at risk" from tropical forest clearing (Bemis and Rising 1999). Riparian habitat is very important, not only for nesting pewees, but as refuge for birds dispersing post-breeding. During July wood-pewees are historically one of the most common birds at the Napa River Ecological Reserve.

DUSKY FLYCATCHER
Empidonax oberholseri

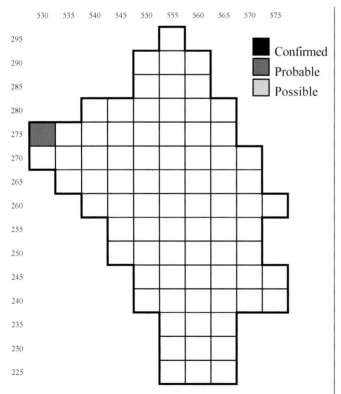

Confirmed
Probable
Possible

Rare summer resident, perhaps not present every year
Only probable May 25 – Multiple observations at
same location

The Dusky Flycatcher is a common bird of the dry interior north Coast Ranges, the Cascades and Sierras. It is found in open chaparral and in chaparral with scattered pines. Grinnell and Miller (1944) describe Mt. Sanhedrin in Mendocino County as the breeding locale nearest to Napa County; it is currently known to breed in Lake County (Yee *et al.* 1992). Since about 1976, Dusky Flycatcher has occasionally been found in Napa during the summer at Haystack Mt. and Mt. St. Helena.

During the Atlas period Dusky Flycatcher was first seen on Mt. St. Helena on July 15, 1990. Between May 10-25, 1992, at least two singing males were found at elevations of 3800 and 4200 feet in brush and sugar pine habitat on the mountain's southeastern slope. On May 25, 1992, singing males were heard at 4200 feet on the Sonoma County side of the mountain as well. Later attempts to relocate the Napa birds were unsuccessful.

Dusky Flycatcher remains unconfirmed as a breeding species in Napa County. It has not been seen at Haystack Mt. since 1986. An abundance of suitable habitat and a more regular pattern of recent occurrence make Mt. St. Helena the most likely breeding location in the county.

PACIFIC-SLOPE FLYCATCHER
Empidonax difficilis

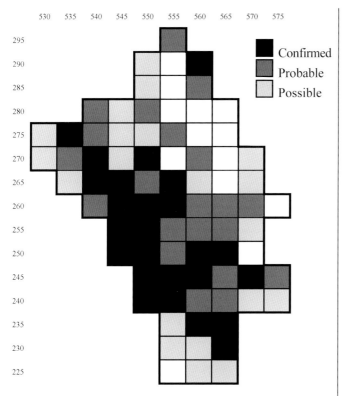

Confirmed
Probable
Possible

Summer resident
Earliest confirmation April 24 – Nest building
Latest confirmation July 4 – Recently fledged young

In dimly lit forest and on shadowy north slopes, the Pacific-slope Flycatcher is a wisp of song and a tiny flash of wings. It is common in steep ravines and narrow canyons throughout the mixed forests above the Napa Valley. It nests in the lowlands as well, tending to favor live oak and bay woodland and older stands of willow and walnut. Nests are placed in a variety of usually shadowy situations: among a recess of roots and stones in a forest road cut, in a shrub or tree, or on the porch of a mountain cabin.

Pacific-slope Flycatcher arrives in Napa at the end of March and by mid-April has established territories in all available habitats. The first of three nest building records was at Bothe on April 24 and the last near Oakville May 28. Eggs were found April 25 at Soda Canyon, with reports June 15 and 16 at Yountville and Redwood Canyon, respectively. Eggs after May are presumed re-nestings or second broods (Lowther 2000). Reports of adults carrying food for young in six blocks span May 1-July 17. Fledglings were found at seven locations beginning May 31 at St. Helena through July 4 near Lake Marie. Probable data of pairs and singing males spans May 9-July 10. County historical records include six egg dates April 20-May 20 and late nests with young July 16 and 29.

Atlasers judged Pacific-slope Flycatcher to be common throughout the county. Areas where birds were scarce or absent simply lacked suitable habitat.

BLACK PHOEBE
Sayornis nigricans

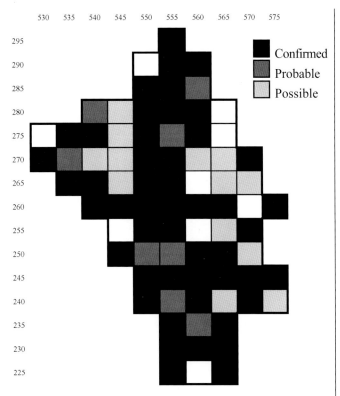

Year-round resident
Earliest confirmation March 22 – Occupied nest
Latest confirmation July 26 – Recently fledged young

An old hunter's camp where a trickling spring filled a bathtub with water for horses was for years enough for a pair of Black Phoebes at Haystack Mt. More typical habitat includes the Napa River, any canyon with permanent water, golf courses, and ranch ponds. A little water and earth for mud to build a nest and a vertical ledge, bank, bridge, or shed for shelter will serve Black Phoebes. They show a moderate dependence on riparian corridors (Wolf 1997).

From an occupied nest along the Sonoma Highway on March 22 to fledglings at Putah Creek on July 26, phoebes were confirmed in 70 percent of the Atlas blocks in which they were found. Seven nest construction reports begin on March 25 at Hardin Creek and continue for 11 weeks. Nestlings were seen at nine locations from May 2 on the east side of Lake Berryessa through June 26 at Snell Valley. Adults carrying food for young were seen in nine blocks April 24-July 3 and fledglings in 12 blocks May 9-July 26. Phoebes regularly raise two broods. Data from research in Santa Clara Co. revealed an early egg date of March 18 and second brood nest completion through May 31 (Wolf 1997). The Atlas data fits well within that phenology.

Phoebes breed throughout the county except for several blocks adjacent to Lake Berryessa and scattered high elevation, heavily forested sites. Since the 1970s, they appear to have newly colonized or increased in numbers in both rural and urban residential areas.

ASH-THROATED FLYCATCHER
Myiarchus cinerascens

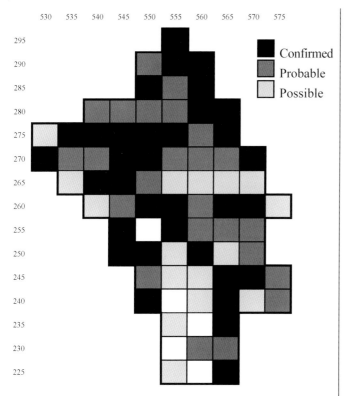

- Confirmed
- Probable
- Possible

Summer resident
Earliest confirmation April 30 – Carrying nesting material
Latest confirmation July 14 – Feeding young

The Ash-throated Flycatcher is the most common member of its family in Napa County. It is found in a variety of wooded habitats, avoiding only dense forests and non-native vegetation. Ash-throated Flycatcher nests in riparian woodland, broken chaparral ridges and canyon slopes, and oak savannah. Unique among our flycatchers, it nests in tree cavities; breeding territories must contain trees large enough to support a cavity. Nest boxes generally increase densities of breeding pairs (Cardiff and Dittmann 2002).

Mated and courting pairs were found during mid-April in three blocks. Additional reports of probable nesting pairs and singing males came from May and June. Nest building was observed at four locations between April 30 at Mt. St. John and May 25 at Knoxville. Four occupied nests were found May 2-July 10. Birds were carrying food for young in 16 blocks: seven throughout May, eight during June through the 22nd, and one on July 1. There were nine reports of fledglings beginning June 1 at Redwood Canyon through July 14 at Aetna Springs.

Ash-throated Flycatcher is widely distributed in the native habitats of Napa County. It is most common during the arid summer in canyon and ridge country of the interior from Milliken canyon north to Swartz Canyon and the Palisades. In the densely forested western hills, flycatchers are usually confined to the chaparral of southern exposures. Because of habitat loss along the Napa River and other riparian corridors, it remains common only at the Napa River Ecological Reserve.

WESTERN KINGBIRD
Tyrannus verticalis

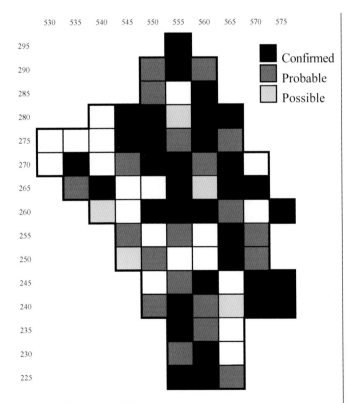

Summer resident
Earliest confirmation April 8 – Carrying nesting material
Latest confirmation July 17 – Carrying food

The Western Kingbird brings a sense of isolation to its surroundings wherever it is found. It is often the only thing moving during the heat of a summer day. Pairs are intolerant of anything resembling a predator, from a scrub-jay to a boy throwing a boomerang. Open land with scattered trees, lowland riparian edges, and small meadows within expanses of brush, oak, and pine are a few of its favored habitats.

Kingbirds frequently arrive on the breeding grounds during the first week of April; individuals carrying nesting material April 8 at Snell Valley and April 11 near Foss Valley may have arrived somewhat earlier than usual. Seven additional nest construction reports span April 20-May 13. Birds carrying food for young in Gordon Valley April 20 and Capell Valley April 26 push back the known season; the earliest egg date reported in Bent (1942) is April 17. Occupied nests in eight blocks span May 2-16. There were seven fledgling reports between May 28 and July 8. Kingbirds continued feeding young July 17 at southwestern Lake Berryessa. Fifteen of the 22 probable records refer to pairs, April 6-July 16.

The accompanying map indicates that Western Kingbird favors the open agricultural pastureland west and south of the city of Napa and the arid upland valleys and meadows of the northeastern half of the county. Nests are relatively rare in the Napa Valley, and the kingbird was absent from riparian breeding sites occupied through 1988 near Oakville and at the Napa River Ecological Reserve.

LOGGERHEAD SHRIKE
Lanius ludovicianus

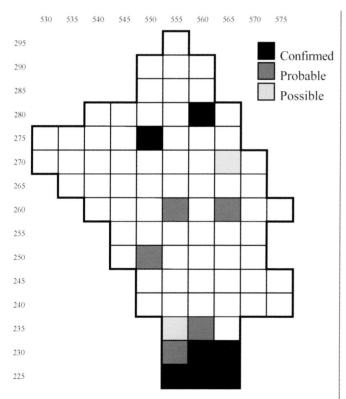

Confirmed
Probable
Possible

Year-round resident, increasingly rare at all seasons in recent years

Earliest confirmation April 29 – Carrying nesting material

Latest confirmation July 3 – Recently fledged young

The Loggerhead Shrike is found in pastures, agricultural fields, golf courses, and grassland. More widespread in the county during winter, it retreats to a few traditional breeding sites early in the spring. Shrikes avoid woodland and areas of continuous cover, including vineyards. Nests are placed in an edge or isolated tree or shrub within the larger habitat. Shrikes persistently re-nest if a clutch of eggs is lost and occasionally raise two broods during a season (Yosef 1996).

Shrikes were confirmed in seven blocks April 29-July 3. Details include carrying nesting material in Jamieson Canyon April 29, a nest containing eggs at northeastern Lake Berryessa May 11, and fledglings at Pope Valley June 8. Fledglings were seen around July 1 in two southern blocks. Pairs observed during April, June, and July represent probable data. Records prior to the Atlas include an occupied nest at the Napa airport February 14 and adults feeding fledglings at Coombsville March 28.

Loggerhead Shrikes maintain a tenuous presence in the county at a handful of traditional sites. Development adjacent to the Napa airport and the conversion of Lewis Dairy to vineyards has marginalized or destroyed two of those sites. Combined Breeding Bird Survey and Christmas Bird Count data 1966-89 shows an annual negative trend in California of 4-6%, among the continent's highest (Yosef 1996). Development, monoculture agriculture, and chemical residues are among the usual suspects. Loggerhead Shrike is a California Species of Special Concern.

CASSIN'S VIREO
Vireo cassinii

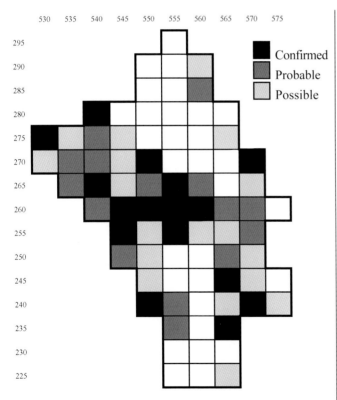

Summer resident
Earliest confirmation May 17 – Occupied nest
Latest confirmation Full Date – Recently fledged
young

The mixed forest of the western hills is the land of vireos, where Cassin's Vireo adds its inventive song to the otherwise rather unimaginative chorus. Cassin's also selects entirely deciduous valley and foothill woodland. Clark (1930) reported it "abundant among the canyon live oaks and in the deeper woods and canyons" surrounding Angwin. In lowland riparian remnants of oak and bay, its abundance once approached that of the western uplands. Cassin's Vireo frequently arrives in the county at the end of March, and by mid-April the nesting season has begun.

Historical records in the lowlands include eggs at the Napa River Ecological Reserve April 23-May 23. In the uplands at Bothe and Los Posadas, egg dates span May 1-31. Atlas nest data includes three occupied nests between May 17 at Conn Valley and June 25 at Wild Horse Valley. Three records of adults carrying food span June 4-28. Fledglings were seen in nine blocks: first at Redwood Canyon on June 2, lastly at St. Helena on July 23. One adult carried nesting material on Mt. St. Helena June 16. The majority of probable data refers to singing males, April 21-June 29.

Cassin's Vireo remains fairly common in the diverse upland forests adjacent to the Napa Valley. It tends to be more local and restricted by habitat suitability east across the interior toward Lake Berryessa. Once common in Valley riparian corridors, Cassin's Vireo is now quite rare as a result of habitat degradation, cowbird parasitism, and nest predation.

HUTTON'S VIREO
Vireo huttoni

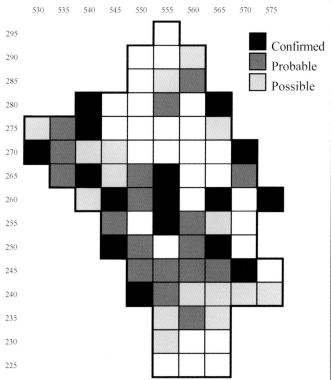

Year-round resident
Earliest confirmation April 9 – Occupied nest
Latest confirmation July 23 – Recently fledged young

The resident vireo in oak woodland in California, Hutton's Vireo paid dearly for its resident status when the freeze of December 1990 resulted in widespread mortality among insectivores throughout Northern California (Yee *et al.* 1991). For the next two years it was difficult simply to find Hutton's Vireo in many areas. The total of three confirmed records during 1991-92 reflects that scarcity. There were five confirmations in 1990 and seven in 1993.

Hutton's Vireo is known to nest in early February in California (Davis 1995), and in Napa County a nearly complete nest was under construction near Murphy Canyon on January 23, 1983. The two earliest Atlas confirmations include an occupied nest at Soda Canyon April 9 and nest building at Wragg Canyon on April 21. Adults were carrying food for young in three blocks May 12-July 3. Fledglings were seen May 14 and 21; six reports span June 4-July 2 and conclude at St. Helena July 23. Probable data refers to pairs and singing males February 20-June 29. There were five Atlas confirmations during July. Documentation of second broods is lacking; July records are presumed to be replacement clutches (Davis 1995).

The distribution of Hutton's Vireo closely follows the presence of oak woodland. The accompanying map reflects the effects of the freeze in areas such as the southeast, where only possible breeding records were obtained despite abundant vireo habitat. Since 1993, vireos have recovered their former numbers in the southeast and throughout the county.

WARBLING VIREO
Vireo gilvus

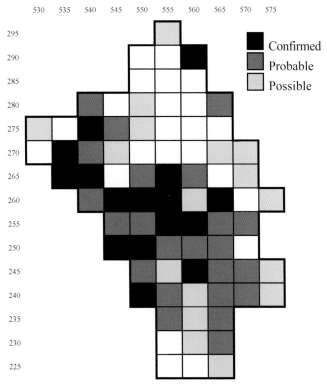

530 535 540 545 550 555 560 565 570 575

295
290
285
280
275
270
265
260
255
250
245
240
235
230
225

■ Confirmed
▨ Probable
▫ Possible

Summer resident
Earliest confirmation April 9 – Nest building
Latest confirmation July 23 – Recently fledged young

Following its arrival at the end of March, the Warbling Vireo soon becomes the most prominent voice along the fire roads throughout the mature mixed forests of the western hills. In company with Cassin's and Hutton's Vireo, the dawn chorus is tremendous. Warbling Vireo can also be found in mature deciduous valley woodland as well as in narrow riparian corridors of willow. It is able to use disjunct patches of habitat and is known to raise second broods in California (Gardali and Ballard 2000).

Atlas records begin with a mated pair in Wooden Valley on March 29. Eighteen similar records continue through May 29, with pairs in an additional five blocks through July 4. Nest construction commenced April 9 at Mt. St. John, followed by a May 1 Redwood Canyon report and May 26 at Calistoga. Adults were carrying food for young in five blocks May 1-July 3. Fledglings were found south of Sage Canyon on June 11; five additional reports extend from June 30 at Chiles Valley through July 23 on the northwestern slope of Atlas Peak. Abundance was estimated at 2-10 pairs in 20 blocks, 11-100 in eight.

Warbling Vireo is fairly common west of Lake Berryessa and Pope Valley. It is absent from arid interior chaparral and open woodland. Long-term research (1979-97) in coastal California indicates a "precipitous decline" for breeding and migratory birds (Gardali and Ballard 2000). While Napa's population may be stable where upland forest remains intact, lowland habitats merit concern.

STELLER'S JAY
Cyanocitta stelleri

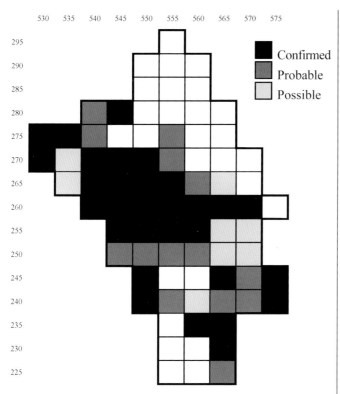

	Confirmed
	Probable
	Possible

Year-round resident
Earliest confirmation March 28 – Nest building
Latest confirmation July 4 – Recently fledged young

The brilliant blue and black Steller's Jay is a common resident of a variety of densely forested mountain canyon and foothill habitats. Most often associated with mixed forests of redwood, fir, and oak, it is also found on steep slopes of live oak and bay and in canyons dominated by alder.

Greene *et al.* (1998) describes April as the peak of nest construction; the seven Atlas records span March 28-May 11. May 25 is the lone egg report. Nestlings at Redwood Canyon April 1 and an occupied nest near Los Posadas April 5 represent early activity. Fledglings were seen in three blocks April 26-May 19 and in 13 blocks May 27-July 4. Mated pairs provided the majority of the Atlas's 14 probable records.

Steller's Jays occupy all of the heart of the county west of Chiles and Capell Valleys, north of Yountville including the western hills, and the higher elevations northwest of Angwin. A second area of concentration is found in the southeast at the blocks bordering Solano County. These two areas provide generally differing habitats. Mixed conifer habitats are widespread in the northwest, while conifers are lacking or confined to major canyons in the southeast. Abundance estimates trend lower at the eastern part of the overall range. These jays are not found in the extensive areas of oak savannah and chaparral bordering Lake Berryessa and northwest toward Knoxville, nor throughout the southwestern tidal and agricultural region.

WESTERN SCRUB-JAY
Aphelocoma californica

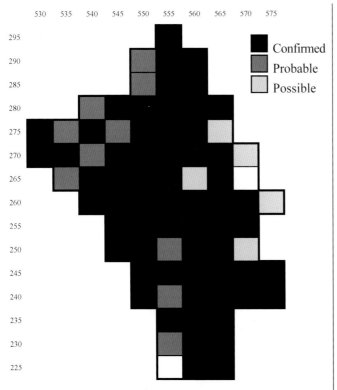

				Confirmed
				Probable
				Possible

Year-round resident
Earliest confirmation February 28 – Carrying nesting material
Latest confirmation July 8 – Feeding young

There are Western Scrub-Jays wherever oaks grow in California. Between the Sierras and the dense coastal forests, they are found in open oak and brushland in mountains, canyons, hills, and valleys. In every town between, jays inhabit most of our shrubby residential neighborhoods. They are successful everywhere and were confirmed breeding in 62 blocks, more than any other species recorded during the Atlas.

The nesting season can begin early. Jays were building nests on February 28 in Carneros Valley and March 16 at St. Helena; an additional seven records span April 20-May 18. A nest with eggs was found along Spring Mountain Road April 11. Nestlings were discovered in two northeastern blocks May 2 and June 1. Adults were carrying food for young in 13 blocks March 29-June 9, with six of the reports May 3-18. Fledgling scrub-jays were seen in 35 blocks April 25-July 8; 24 reports May 20-June 29 indicate the peak interval. Abundance estimates exceeded ten pairs in almost all of the 42 reporting blocks.

Steller's Jay usually replaces Western Scrub-Jay in the shadowy mixed forests of the western hills and at higher elevations in northern Napa Valley. The two jays often occur together in areas such as the thickly forested slopes of live oak in the southeastern hills and in the large canyons east of the Valley. In the end, however, the scrub-jay prefers brush and live oak (Grinnell and Miller 1944). Where conditions are right, Western Scrub-Jay is the primary source of avian motion and sound.

Sponsored by Art Battiste in memory of Aliece Battiste

YELLOW-BILLED MAGPIE
Pica nuttalli

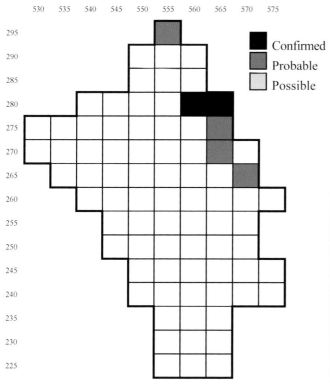

■ Confirmed
▨ Probable
░ Possible

Year-round resident
Earliest confirmation May 1 – Occupied nest
Latest confirmation May 2 – Nest with young

It may come as a surprise to many to learn of the small resident population of Yellow-billed Magpie confined almost exclusively to the ranches and oak savannah at the eastern and northern shores of Lake Berryessa. The species is common across the mountains ten miles east in the Sacramento Valley. Linsdale (1937) and Reynolds (1995) each describe its absence in the Coast Range north of San Francisco Bay. The birds at Berryessa are probably the descendants of those that lived in the Monticello Valley prior to the construction of the dam. Valley and live oaks are favored nest sites, and magpies require water throughout the year (Reynolds 1995).

Magpies were found in six priority blocks and confirmed in two. An occupied nest was discovered at the northern tip of Lake Berryessa May 1, 1990, and a nest with young was found along the western slope of Blue Ridge at the lake on May 2, 1993. Mated pairs were observed in three additional east-side Berryessa blocks during three different years between May 3 and June 11 and at Knoxville on May 1, 1990.

Historically, Linsdale (1937) pointed out that Fisher (1900) only suspected magpies on Mt. St. Helena; there are no records west of Lake Berryessa. In the recent past, magpies were both persecuted as an agricultural pest and killed unintentionally where compound 1080 was used to control ground squirrels (Reynolds 1995). The "previously unknown" Berryessa population of this California endemic is under no such direct threat.

AMERICAN CROW
Corvus brachyrhynchos

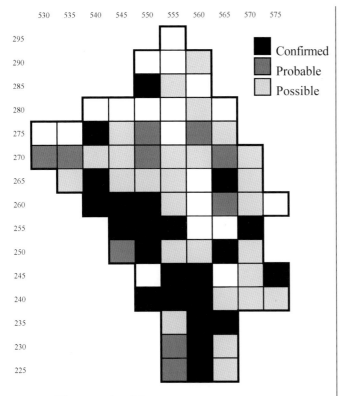

Year-round resident
Earliest confirmation March 20 – Carrying nesting material
Latest confirmation July 3 – Feeding young

Open and boisterous during most of the year, the American Crow becomes remarkably quiet and passive while raising young. Even a bird crossing open country carrying a stick for a nest appears furtive, pretending to be invisible. In 1923 William Dawson described the crow in California as "sharply restricted in distribution, rather a novelty, something to be jotted down in the field-book" (Bent 1946). Today, crows are found almost everywhere, preferring our settled landscapes throughout the year. During the nesting season, open urban and rural environments provide abundant food and a variety of native and exotic trees in which to nest and roost.

Six nest construction records span March 20-April 6, with four additional reports May 4-30. Nests were occupied in seven blocks beginning April 11 southeast of Atlas Peak, through May 30 in the city of Napa. A nest with young was found at Coombsville on June 7. Three blocks reported fledglings, June 21-July 3. Except for one report of courtship, probable records are represented by mated pairs, April 28-July 20.

Based upon confirmations, the American Crow appears most common along the Napa River. However, abundance estimates are equal or slightly greater east of the Napa Valley. Knight *et al.* (1987) found that American Crow nest defense strategies differ between areas of high and low human population. Crows in populated areas are more defensive and remain near the nest longer, increasing the chance of its detection by humans. Rural crows are wilier, and nest detection is reduced.

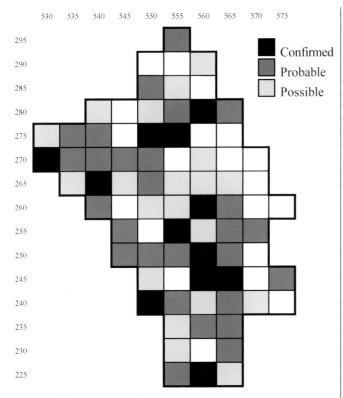

Confirmed

Probable

Possible

Year-round resident
Earliest confirmation March 24 – Occupied nest
Latest confirmation July 4 – Carrying food

Much has changed since Grinnell and Miller (1944) described the Common Raven as "now scarce or absent in all settled parts of the State." Often a symbol of wild seacoast and interior canyons, ravens forage widely and today are common over the Napa Valley and its towns, taking advantage of refuse and road kills. Breeding areas remain somewhat removed from human habitation at upland canyons, cliffs, and rock outcrops, as well as around the southern tidal marshes.

Ravens in California lay eggs during March-late May, with young in the nest by mid-June (Bent 1946, Boarman and Heinrich 1999). Atlas data reflects the known phenology: four occupied nests between March 24 west of Napa Junction and April 29 southeast of Lake Hennessey; four nests with young beginning May 24 at Eticuera Creek, through June 3 in the Bothe area. Atlasers found nestlings in adjacent blocks on May 25, 1989: at Soda Canyon and at a ranch off Silverado Trail. Adults were observed feeding fledglings at lower Chiles Valley on June 28. Probable data refers primarily to pairs seen during May and early June. Possible data, March 10-July 20, describes individuals in suitable breeding habitat.

Common Raven is resident throughout the county. Nesting pairs forage over great distances, so it might not breed in every block with probable and possible records. Someday it may, since the raven is at least as clever as we are.

HORNED LARK
Eremophila alpestris

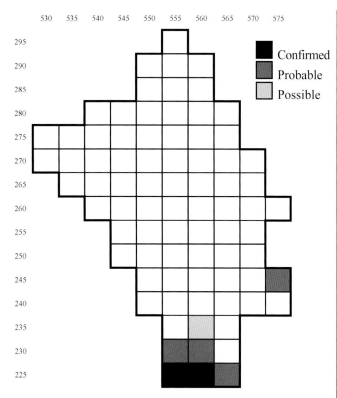

Year-round resident, more numerous in winter
Earliest confirmation May 26 – Carrying food
Latest confirmation June 15 – Carrying food

The resident Horned Lark is found on barren ground year-round. Overgrazed pastures, alkali flats, and the edges of airport runways provide such habitat. Suitably denuded sites are uncommon in the county. Several distinctive races of Horned Lark breed in California (Bent 1942), with Napa County lying at the periphery of the range of three widespread forms. It is unclear which occurs here, and intergrades are possible.

Except for a mated pair on the shore of Lake Curry on May 2, 1990, larks were confined to six pasture and tideland blocks immediately south of the city of Napa. Confirmations include adults carrying food for young at Huichica Creek Wildlife Area, June 15, 1989, and again near the county airport on May 26, 1991. Mated or courting pairs were observed in nearby blocks during May and June.

Breeding records prior to the Atlas are confined to Huichica Creek and Stanly Ranch. Larks have also been found during the summer at the grazed pastures east of the county airport. Each of these areas has been altered since the conclusion of the Atlas: manipulation of water leaves the alkali flats at Huichica permanently flooded; grazing has ceased and the industrial park installed east of the airport; and vineyards have replaced grazing lands at Stanly Ranch. Horned Lark is a Species of Special Concern in California. The pastureland west of Milton Road is today the best place to find Horned Larks throughout the year.

PURPLE MARTIN
Progne subis

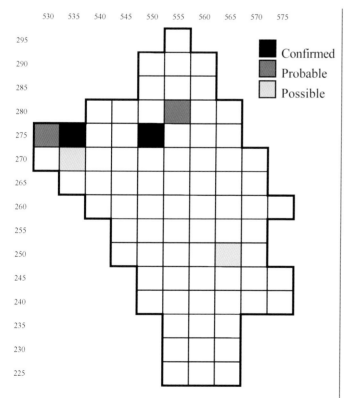

Summer resident
Earliest confirmation June 3 – Nest with young
Latest confirmation July 1 – Nest with young

Confirmed
Probable
Possible

The discovery of a Purple Martin in Napa County almost certainly marks the location of a nesting territory. Migrants or post-breeding wanderers are rarely encountered. Martin habitat includes mixed chaparral and conifer slopes at high elevations. The upper reaches of broad open canyons and rocky ridges are favored, where isolated stands of living or dead Douglas fir provide the most commonly used nest sites. Unlike Purple Martins of eastern North America, the mountain west subspecies, *P.s. arboricola*, does not frequent human habitation. Its winter range is unknown but may include Brazil and Bolivia (Turner and Rose 1989).

Nestling Purple Martins were found near Table Rock on June 3, 1992, and at Pope Valley July 1, 1993. The martins in Pope Valley nested in an old Acorn Woodpecker cavity in a utility pole; to this day martins nest in that cavity. An observer located an occupied nest southeast of Deer Park on June 6, 1993. Mated pairs were found on Mt. St. Helena, July 1, 1989, and at upper Putah Creek, May 17, 1993. During 1993 individual martins were seen southeast of Atlas Peak May 22 and at the Palisades July 27.

The Atlas records away from the three extreme northwestern blocks are in areas where Purple Martin was previously unknown. Throughout the northwest, Douglas fir killed in the 1964 fires supported the nests of generations of martins. The species' overall range has contracted as those trees have fallen. The breeding population in Napa County probably does not exceed 30 pairs.

TREE SWALLOW
Tachycineta bicolor

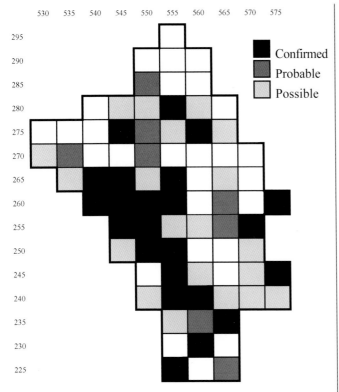

530 535 540 545 550 555 560 565 570 575

■ Confirmed
▨ Probable
□ Possible

Year-round resident
Earliest confirmation April 3 – Occupied nest
Latest confirmation June 28 – Occupied nest

Found in small flocks throughout the winter in tidal marshes of the south, Tree Swallows venture north very early in spring into the valleys and foothills. They prefer more open country than the equally common Violet-green Swallow, and the breeding season tends to be earlier as well. Nests are placed in natural or artificial cavities, usually near rivers, lakes, or ponds.

Tree Swallows were building nests at five Napa Valley locations April 11-June 20. Occupied nests were found on April 3 and 5 at Aetna Springs and Oakville, respectively, and June 28 at Angwin; eight additional reports span April 23-June 1. Adults were carrying food for young in four blocks May 28-June 18. Perhaps owing to their wide-ranging foraging behavior (into blocks where they may not breed), a rather high 39 percent of records were possible records, all referring to birds judged flying over suitable breeding habitat.

The range of the Tree Swallow is concentrated in the Napa Valley between Calistoga and the city of Napa. In addition, priority blocks in the Pope, Capell, and Gordon Valleys and the Putah Creek arm of Lake Berryessa support populations judged by atlasers to be 11-100 pairs. Tree Swallows avoid the higher elevations and heavily vegetated regions of the interior east as well as the western hills.

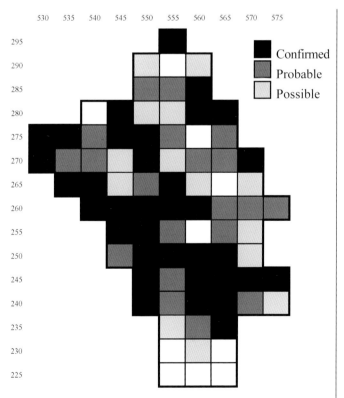

530 535 540 545 550 555 560 565 570 575

295 290 285 280 275 270 265 260 255 250 245 240 235 230 225

■ Confirmed
▨ Probable
□ Possible

Summer resident, rare winter visitor
Earliest confirmation April 5 – Occupied nest
Latest confirmation July 7 – Occupied nest

The Violet-green Swallow is our mountain canyon and forest swallow; it also nests in wooded lowland areas where it flies with its near relative, the Tree Swallow. It avoids open tidal marshes as well as hard chaparral slopes. Suitable nest sites include tree cavities, the occasional nest box, and rock crevices. Small colonies develop at favored sites such as the great pitted boulders above Swartz Canyon, where a dozen nests can be found in close proximity. Violet-green Swallow is occasionally found in the Napa Marsh during winter; spring migrants are widespread by late February.

Occupied nests near Oakville on the fifth and Foss Valley on the eleventh initiate the season and were the only April confirmations. Five additional April records refer to mated pairs. Swallows presented the range of confirming behaviors during May and June. Six nest construction records span May 4-21. Nine of 13 occupied nests were found between May 29 and July 7. Nestlings were discovered at Pope Valley, Milliken, and Chiles Valley May 31-June 28. Fledglings in five blocks span June 9-July 4. Probable reports refer primarily to mated pairs April 1-July 27. Abundance was estimated in 61 percent of confirmed blocks. Atlasers reported 11-100 pairs in two-thirds of them.

Violet-green Swallow is common throughout the county, except for the far south and scattered blocks northeast of the Napa Valley. The somewhat weaker breeding evidence across the range of blocks along the western fringe of Lake Berryessa may be attributable to a shortage of suitable nest sites.

NORTHERN ROUGH-WINGED SWALLOW
Stelgidopteryx serripennis

EDWARD ROOKS ©2001

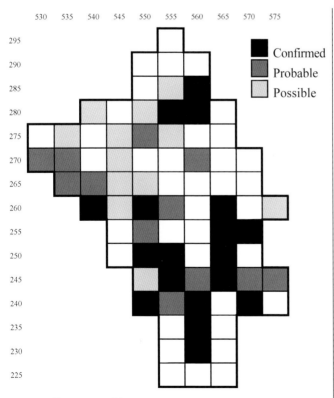

Confirmed
Probable
Possible

Summer resident
Earliest confirmation April 28 – Nest building
Latest confirmation June 21 – Feeding young

While it often arrives in the county by March 15, the Northern Rough-winged Swallow rarely begins its breeding cycle before May 1. Favoring open country, it nests in earthen burrows at stream banks and road cuts, in crevices in bridges and stony cliffs, and occasionally in cracks in buildings. Nest sites are not restricted to areas near water (DeJong 1996). Bent (1942) and Baicich and Harrison (1997) state that rough-wingeds excavate their own burrows; however, DeJong (1996) concludes that ornithologists do not know for certain if such is the case.

Nest construction was reported at five locations April 28-May 28. Five occupied nests span May 3-June 2. A nest with young was found June 13 at Lake Hennessey. Fledglings in five blocks after May 25 include the final confirmation on June 21 at the southwestern shore of Lake Berryessa. Probable reports describe mated and courting pairs, primarily April 25-July 5. Mated pairs were also at Lake Curry April 8 and Calistoga April 9.

As is the case with most North American swallow species, Northern Rough-winged Swallow has generally benefited from human endeavor, exploiting nest sites where none existed prior to settlement. While nest sites have been created, they have also been lost to stream bank stabilization projects. Suitable burrows are the limiting factor for breeding rough-wingeds, and tubular artificial burrows have been successful (DeJong 1996). Lake Berryessa is perhaps a suitable site for such a project - swallows were not found at seven blocks touching the lake shore.

CLIFF SWALLOW
Petrochelidon pyrrhonota

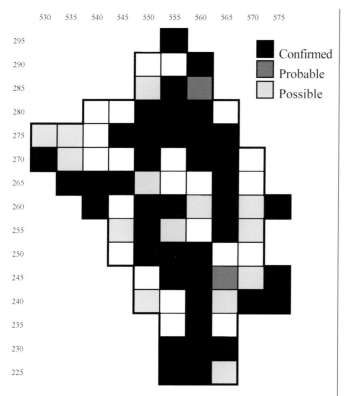

Confirmed
Probable
Possible

Summer resident
Earliest confirmation March 20 – Carrying nesting material
Latest confirmation July 19 – Occupied nest

The Cliff Swallow has apparently abandoned the canyon and outcrop colony sites it must have used in Napa prior to European settlement. Structures of cement and stone - courthouses and bridges - supply the overhang upon which it attaches its spectacular nest. Cliff Swallows generally forage over open country, or high in the "aero plankton" zone of the sky, a world beyond our understanding. They require mud as building material, the source of which may be "several kilometers" away from the colony (Brown & Brown 1995).

Nine of the 12 Atlas nest building records span April 26-June 9; March 20 and July 5 represent early and late dates. Atlasers peeked into nine nests and found young May 30-June 18; one nest sheltered nestlings on July 4. Occupied nests in 12 of 14 blocks span April 27-June 1; April 13 and July 19 represent the extremes. Cliff Swallow breeding sites are conspicuous, so the species is relatively easy to confirm early in the season. Perhaps as a result, fledglings were reported in just two blocks, May 25 and July 3. Estimates of abundance from 27 blocks were all greater than 11 pairs. Six blocks - North Kelly Rd., Gordon Valley, upper Eticuera Creek, and the three large bridges at northwestern Lake Berryessa - held 101-1000 pairs.

Swallows were absent from densely vegetated upland blocks such as Dry Creek, the Palisades, and Cedar Roughs. Many blocks probably lack suitable nest sites. Inexplicably, Coombsville, Carneros, and Linda Vista did not support breeding swallows.

BARN SWALLOW
Hirundo rustica

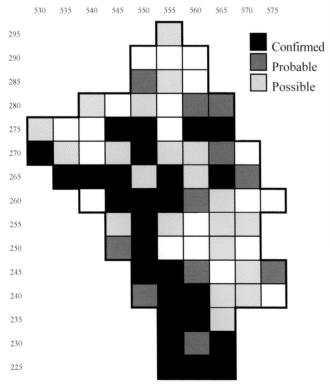

Summer resident
Earliest confirmation March 28 – Nest building
Latest confirmation August 28 – Nest with young

Before Napans built their wonderful stone bridges and other structures of less architectural distinction, the Barn Swallow was a bird of caves and rock crevices (Grinnell and Miller 1944). Since mainland California's settlement, it has converted entirely to nesting upon or within artificial structures (Brown and Brown 1999). In addition, it prefers the presence of water and sky in open country and a source of mud with which to construct nests.

Barn Swallows are frequent in late March; however, during most springs they are uncommon until April is well along. Therefore, two 1990 records in adjacent mid-Napa Valley blocks are unusual: nest building on March 28 and an occupied nest on April 1. The earliest California egg date reported in Bent (1942) is April 9. More expected, six of the seven additional nest building reports span May 1-30, with occupied nests in seven blocks April 16-June 9. Nestlings were found at six locations May 17-June 30, and fledglings at three May 31-June 18. Among the three Atlas confirmations after mid-June, a Pope Valley nest held young on August 28, the third brood raised in that nest that summer.

Barn Swallows are most common the length of the Napa Valley, Pope Valley, Lake Berryessa, the city of Napa, and in the tidal district. Possible data is represented by birds in potential habitat, primarily in the eastern interior of the county where habitat needs of water and nest sites are often limited. Swallows were absent from high-elevation and heavily vegetated blocks.

 Sponsored by Christian Brothers Justin Community

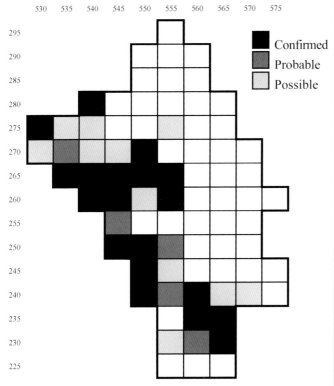

Year-round resident
Earliest confirmation March 11 – Carrying nesting material
Latest confirmation July 4 – Feeding young

Early in the spring, mated pairs of Chestnut-backed Chickadees leave their winter flocks, define a territory, and raise a family. Chickadees are common in coniferous and mixed forests, primarily where Douglas fir and redwood occur; but they also nest in lowland riparian woodland, upland live oak, alder canyons, and even in cities where ornamental conifers flourish. Advances into oak woodland may be limited by competition with the Oak Titmouse (Harrap and Quinn 1995).

Chickadees carrying nesting material near the Bale Grist Mill on March 11 illustrate the early onset of the season. Nest building was also observed in the city of Napa on May 16. Occupied nests were found at Bothe on May 1 and in the north Napa block on May 12. Three records of adults carrying food for young span May 1-19; a fourth was obtained June 25. Fledglings were seen in nine blocks between May 22 at Redwood Canyon and July 4 at Lake Marie. Each of five probable records refers to mated pairs, March 30-July 5. Abundance reports from 21 blocks were mixed between 2-10 and 11-100 pairs; a cluster of five blocks southeast of Angwin reported the lower estimate.

Grinnell and Miller (1944) describe Mt. St. Helena and Howell Mt. as the southeastern limit of the chickadee range in Napa County. While certainly present farther south even then, Chestnut-backed Chickadees have made small advances into settled areas and are today resident in planted redwood groves south to Napa Valley College.

Sponsored by Phil and Dee Dee Sary

OAK TITMOUSE
Baeolophus inornatus

The Oak Titmouse is a model of stability. Pairs are sedentary, maintain their territory throughout the year, and mate for life (Cicero 2000). Titmice prefer oak woodland habitat; they are also found at edges in mixed Douglas fir forests and in open oak-chaparral with foothill pine. Titmice can thrive in residential areas where oaks persist and nest sites are available. In Alta Heights, one pair or another has nested annually for almost 30 years in an oak with a nest box.

Titmice nest early. March 12 was the average date to commence nest building in Alta Heights 1975-88. During the Atlas, extremes of nest construction are Feb. 21 at St. Helena and May 31 at Pope Valley. Seven occupied nests span March 14-June 25. Adults carried food for young in 11 blocks April 22-May 3, and in three May 15-27. Fledglings were near Bothe April 5, in eight blocks during May, and at 19 locations June 3-July 12. Western Foundation of Vertebrate Zoology records contain no egg date after early May (Cicero 2000); several Atlas records appear to fall outside expectations. However, the interval between egg laying and fledging is about 32 days, and young remain with parents 3-4 weeks (Harrap and Quinn 1995). Monterey County's Atlas reported nest building during June (Cicero 2000).

In suitable habitat where natural cavities or boxes offer nest sites, Oak Titmouse is a common bird. Several blocks were believed to support more than 100 pairs, including Soda Canyon, northeast Napa, southern Pope Valley, and upper Putah Creek.

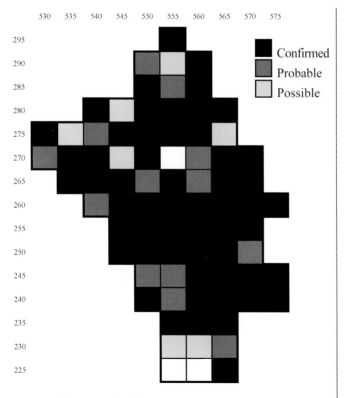

■ Confirmed
▨ Probable
□ Possible

Year-round resident
Earliest confirmation February 21 – Nest building
Latest confirmation July 12 – Feeding young

Sponsored by Frank Stout

BUSHTIT
Psaltriparus minimus

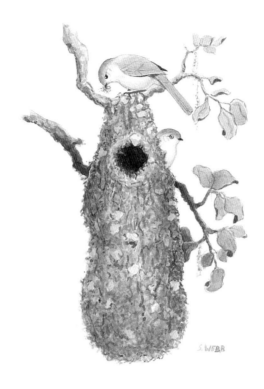

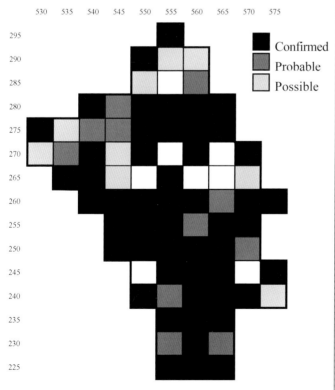

Year-round resident
Earliest confirmation March 12 – Nest building
Latest confirmation July 18 – Recently fledged young

A mated pair of Bushtits remains active in a flock throughout the nesting season. Nest construction may take more than a month, and, after egg laying, the nest is not defended from other flock members that steal nesting material and even enter the nest (Sloane 2001). Bushtits inhabit all types of open oak woodland associations including riparian groves, mountain chaparral, mixed conifers, and backyard gardens. They are adaptable to altered conditions, nesting near sea level at Kennedy Park and foraging along the coyote-bush-covered levees of Napa Marsh.

The Napa nesting season is typically well along by March; a pair was carrying nesting material at Wragg Ridge March 13. The last of an additional eight reports came from Rector Canyon May 16. Four occupied nests were found April 2-May 1, and nestlings were reported at Napa and Pope Canyon on May 7 and 31, respectively. Bushtits carried food for young in eight blocks April 20-May 28. Fledglings in 25 blocks span April 24-July 18, with 21 records during May-June. Bushtit was judged common over most of the county; however, estimates tended lower in the far south and the far north.

Bushtit populations tend to fluctuate and may decline in areas where oak woodland is reduced (Sloane 2001). Atlas results may have pinpointed a decline related to the December 1990 freeze. Following 11 and 12 confirmations in 1989 and 1990, respectively, there were six confirmations in 1991. If that drop was related to the freeze, the 17 confirmations in 1992 indicate a rapid recovery.

RED-BREASTED NUTHATCH
Sitta canadensis

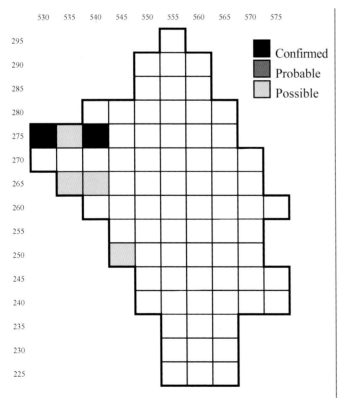

Confirmed
Probable
Possible

Rare year-round resident
Earliest confirmation July 14 – Recently fledged young
Latest confirmation July 15 – Recently fledged young

The piping note of the Red-breasted Nuthatch is an uncommon sound during the summer in the county's upland forests. In fact, the red-breast is a rarity here at all seasons. Nesting habitat is described as red and white fir forest in the Canadian Life Zone (Grinnell and Miller 1944) and "mixed woodland with a strong coniferous element" (Harrap and Quinn 1995). The habitat at the two Atlas breeding sites was described as mixed oak and Douglas fir on steep slopes.

Bill Grummer and Robin Leong's discovery of fledglings near Aetna Springs on July 14, 1990, represents the first breeding record in Napa County. The next day on Mt. St. Helena Mr. Grummer again found fledglings. An individual adult nuthatch on May 6, 1990, near Table Rock links the two blocks where breeding was confirmed. There were three additional Atlas records: a male in the Diamond Mt. block May 18, 1989, an adult at Bothe May 23, 1991, and an adult near Mt. St. John June 3, 1990.

Grinnell and Miller (1944) describe Lake County's Cobb Mt. as the southern extent of the breeding range in the north Coast Range. Since then, Bay Area breeding records are few and of local occurrence (William G. Bousman, unpubl. data, Ghalambor and Martin 1999). R. Leong (unpubl. data) describes them as "nonresident irruptive." The fact that most Atlas records are from 1990 tends to support that statement. The presence of Red-breasted Nuthatch in Napa County during the breeding season is unreliable.

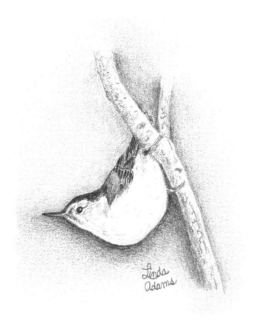

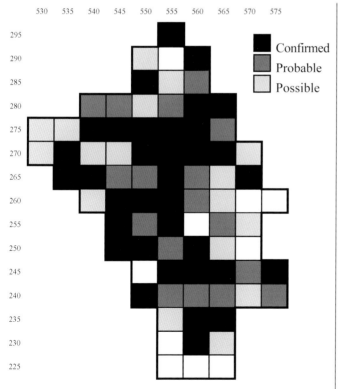

- Confirmed
- Probable
- Possible

Year-round resident
Earliest confirmation March 21 – Nest building
Latest confirmation July 18 – Recently fledged young

The most common and widespread of our three nuthatches, the White-breasted Nuthatch is a permanent resident of oak and mixed deciduous forests across the county. It is a frequent garden feeder visitor as well and will occasionally use a nest box. Pairs maintain permanent territories during the year (Pradosudov and Grubb 1993), and with patience an observer can usually locate the mate of every lone nuthatch. Unlike our other nuthatches, the white-breasted does not excavate its own nest, preferring a pre-existing cavity.

Atlas reports begin on the first day of spring, when nuthatches were building nests at lower Soda Canyon and Mt. St. John on March 21. Nest building was observed in three other blocks April 2-May 2. Adults were carrying food for young in eight blocks April 6-June 10. Nestlings were found near Calistoga April 12 and on Lake Berryessa's east side May 3. Fledglings were reported in 15 blocks May 20-July 18; nine such records span May 30-June 20 and four were in July. Probable reports include courtship February 26 at Wooden Valley and mated pairs in 11 blocks March 23-June 29.

The White-breasted Nuthatch was either absent or breeding evidence was relatively weak from three clusters of priority blocks. Records of possible nesting came from five high-elevation or ponderosa-pine-dominated blocks stretching east from Mt. St. Helena. Black oak foothills south of Lake Berryessa lacked nuthatches in four blocks. Their absence from the unforested southern marshes is not surprising.

Sponsored by Peter and Carlene Mennen

PYGMY NUTHATCH
Sitta pygmaea

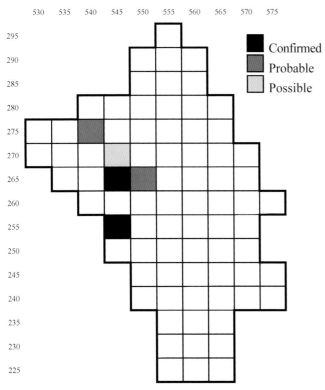

530 535 540 545 550 555 560 565 570 575

295
290
285
280
275
270
265
260
255
250
245
240
235
230
225

■ Confirmed
▨ Probable
▢ Possible

Year-round resident
Only confirmation July 5 – Feeding young

The range of the Pygmy Nuthatch parallels the distribution of ponderosa pine forest in Napa County. Old growth forest provides optimal habitat, and there is a direct relationship between the density of pine foliage and Pygmy Nuthatch density; i.e., breeding territories are larger where pines are fewer (Kingery and Ghalambor 2001). Norris (1958) mapped a 3.7-acre nuthatch territory on Howell Mountain, 30 percent larger than the average in Marin County, where canopy cover was six times greater. Pygmy Nuthatch frequently nests cooperatively, and helpers at the nest, usually yearling males, may decrease nest predation (Harrap and Quinn 1995).

Mated pairs of Pygmy Nuthatch were west of Aetna Springs and southeast of Angwin May 25 and June 26, respectively. The Pacific Union College campus held an undated 1992 occupied nest. Adults were feeding fledglings at the western end of Lewelling Lane in St. Helena on July 5, 1991. This relatively low-elevation site, somewhat removed from the core Angwin range, was in an isolated stand of ponderosa pine. Pygmy Nuthatches have been present for many years and also use Douglas fir forests upslope (A. Wight, pers. comm.).

Pygmy Nuthatch is an engaging, social bird. Winter flocks of 5-20 frequent the Angwin area during winter. Such flocks roost communally in tree cavities (Norris 1958). In a diverse ponderosa pine forest community, the dying and decaying trees, which provide critical Pygmy Nuthatch nesting and roosting sites, are of primary importance.

BROWN CREEPER
Certhia americana

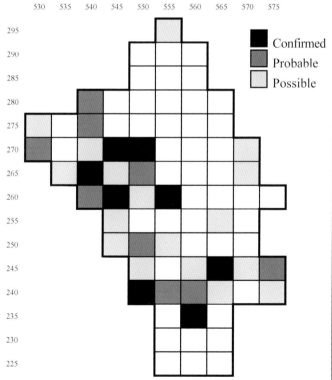

Year-round resident, more widespread in winter
Earliest confirmation May 1 – Carrying nesting material
Latest confirmation July 2 – Recently fledged young

Inhabiting the largest trees in dense forest or in open wood-land, the Brown Creeper is at once camouflaged and dwarfed by its surroundings. In the hills above the Napa Valley floor, creepers are found in mixed forests of redwood, oak, and fir. Birds in the Napa Valley nest in open old-growth oak woodland, where nests are placed behind plates of loosened bark of dead trees. In Napa's coniferous forests, nesting substrate is typically living coast redwoods. The presence of nest sites "may be the critical limiting factor in its distribution" (Harrap and Quinn 1997).

The eight probable reports of mated pairs span April 5-July 4. Creepers were discovered building nests at Bothe on May 1, St. Helena May 9, and near Angwin May 16. Birds were observed carrying food for young at Napa, Pope Valley, and Milliken, May 13-June 22. Fledglings were seen at Redwood Canyon on May 22 and northeast of Lake Hennessey on July 2. At the Napa River Ecological Reserve 1980-88, seven records of occupied nests or nestlings span April 2-June 20, with nestlings as early as April 16. Nest-building records there span March 6-April 2, and include four records during March 2000.

Brown Creeper habitat in the upland forests remains relatively extensive. However, creepers occur there at low densities, and forest fragmentation may pose a significant threat. Lowland creepers are confined to small patches of increasingly vulnerable habitat where the primary component of that habitat, the valley oak, is vanishing.

ROCK WREN
Salpinctes obsoletus

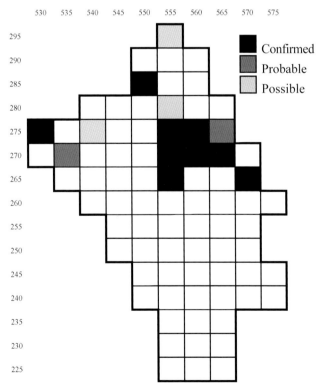

Year-round resident
Earliest confirmation May 2 – Carrying food
Latest confirmation July 18 – Carrying food

Broad slopes or canyon sides of broken rock and fields of stone in the mountains provide the Rock Wren with the basics of life. Such areas in the county have meager soils or none at all, and vegetation is limited to gnarled dwarf oaks and patches of chaparral. Its fondness for remote, barren landscapes is revealed in its being a common resident of the Farallon Islands (Bent 1948). During winter, many Rock Wrens descend to the shores of Lake Berryessa, where they forage amid the driftwood or upon fallen oaks in open fields.

Rock Wrens were confirmed in nine blocks where fledglings were seen or birds were observed carrying food for their young. Adults were first detected with food at southeastern Lake Berryessa May 2. Parents were likewise engaged in three adjacent blocks in the Putah Creek and Pope Canyon region July 5-18. Adults with fledglings were on the east side of Berryessa on June 20, and newly fledged birds were at Mt. St. Helena and upper Putah Creek during mid-July. Wrens were also found at Knoxville, Swartz Canyon, the Palisades, and above Chiles Valley.

Rock Wrens were judged most common in the two blocks encompassing the Pope and Putah Creek arms of Lake Berryessa. Mt. St. Helena and the Palisades support an additional isolated population. Birds were not found during the Atlas period at Haystack Mt. or Milliken Canyon, where there were several breeding records during the 1980s.

CANYON WREN
Catherpes mexicanus

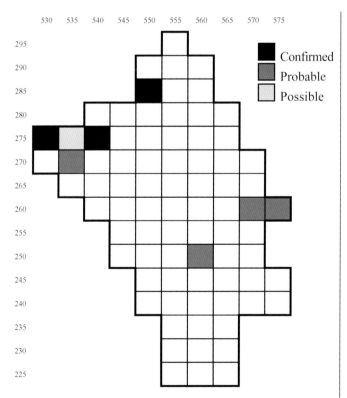

530 535 540 545 550 555 560 565 570 575

■ Confirmed
▨ Probable
□ Possible

Year-round resident
Earliest confirmation June 16 – Occupied nest
Latest confirmation July 11 – Recently fledged young

The Canyon Wren inhabits some of the most rugged and spectacular places in Napa County. It is found on the canyon walls of Rector and Milliken and the cliffs of the Palisades and Mt. St. Helena. Pairs are also found at ridge-top outcrops and in boulder fields within expanses of chaparral. Its association with rock monoliths is such that its "occurrence is not correlated with any vegetative community" (Jones & Dieni 1995).

Canyon Wren was confirmed in three of the five northwestern blocks in which it was found. An occupied nest was discovered at Mt. St. Helena on June 16, 1989; fledglings were seen at upper Putah Creek on July 11, 1991; and adults were tending fledglings west of Aetna Springs on July 3, 1993. In addition, Canyon Wrens were found in the two blocks that contain the Palisades. To the southeast, singing males were at Wragg Canyon and Monticello Dam in May, and territorial birds were observed southwest of Atlas Peak during early June.

The Atlas reports reflect known traditional locations of Canyon Wren in the county. Several sites in and around Milliken Canyon also support these wrens, but birds were not found there during Atlas fieldwork. Most of these areas are isolated and remote, and densities are very low due to the species' narrow habitat preference. The most accessible sites to see and hear Canyon Wrens are Monticello Dam and along the Palisades and Mt. St. Helena trails.

Sponsored by Tom and Pat Hildreth

BEWICK'S WREN
Thryomanes bewickii

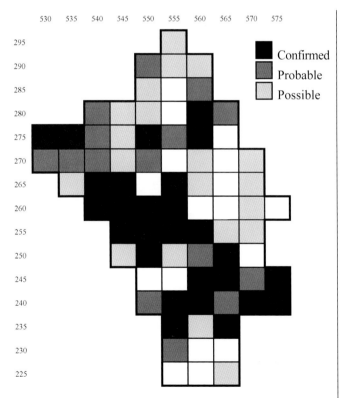

Year-round resident
Earliest confirmation April 16 – Carrying food
Latest confirmation August 3 – Recently fledged
young

■ Confirmed
▨ Probable
☐ Possible

Of our two widespread breeding upland wrens, Bewick's and House, Bewick's Wren is the resident species, brightening even the grimmest winter day with its richly varied song. Most abundant in chaparral and riparian thickets, it is also found around human dwellings, especially where the vegetation is unkempt. It will occasionally use a nest box; however, the skimpiest of cavities will suffice (Kennedy and White 1997). The Atlas did not collect data regarding the use of artificial structures.

Bewick's Wren enjoys a lengthy nesting season, as evidenced by an adult carrying food on April 16 southeast of Lake Hennessey and an Aug. 3 report of fledglings at Spencer Creek. Just under two-thirds of all probable and confirmed data spans Apr. 27-June 4. Eggs were reported at Bothe on May 8 and nestlings on the western slope of Mt. George June 1. On May 5 Rutherford had the first of 15 fledgling reports. Eighty percent of probable data describes singing males or pairs.

Found throughout the county, Bewick's Wren was most frequently confirmed west of a line from Mt. St. Helena, through Angwin, to Gordon Valley. Wrens are most thinly distributed or frequently absent in blocks to the east. Large areas of open blue and black oak woodland, the agricultural area of Pope Valley, and the open shores of Lake Berryessa do not provide optimum habitat. Wrens were also scarce in the southernmost six blocks of marsh and agricultural land where suitable habitat is minimal.

Sponsored by David Takeuchi

HOUSE WREN
Troglodytes aedon

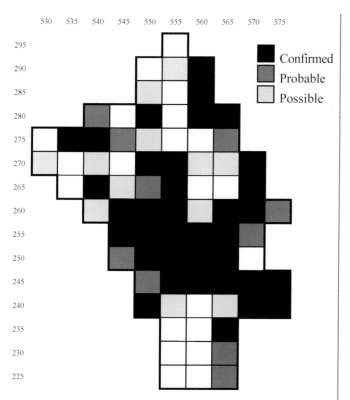

	530	535	540	545	550	555	560	565	570	575

- ■ Confirmed
- ▨ Probable
- ☐ Possible

Summer resident, rare winter visitor
Earliest confirmation April 3 – Carrying nesting material
Latest confirmation July 18 – Recently fledged young

During the years following the 1980 Atlas Peak fire, the House Wren became the most common breeding species across the scorched chaparral, oak, and foothill pine slopes above Rector and Milliken Canyons. When not taking advantage of fire, it is most common in riparian areas, open deciduous canyons, and oak savannah. House Wren arrives in the county during the last week of March. A few overwinter each year.

Observations of nest building activity commence April 3 (at Pope Valley) and continue during the month through the 19th. A second interval of nest construction spans May 2-June 2. An occupied nest in Soda Canyon on April 21 preceded four others May 15-June 1. Ten records of adults carrying food for young span May 10-June 13; one at Capell Valley on April 11 is early. Records of eggs in California before April are rare (Johnson 1998). Fledglings were found near St. Helena and Oakville on April 30 and May 5, respectively, and in eight additional blocks June 13-July 18.

The heart of the House Wren's county range remains the middle elevation hills and canyons east of the Napa Valley between St. Helena and Lake Curry. House Wrens are reliably found on the Valley floor in remnants of the riparian corridor, as well as in the blue oak foothills east of Lake Berryessa. They are absent from extensive chaparral and agricultural regions, and, unlike their eastern North America counterparts, they tend to avoid residential neighborhoods.

WINTER WREN
Troglodytes troglodytes

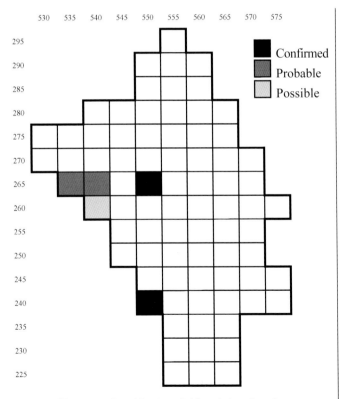

Confirmed

Probable

Possible

Year-round resident, variable winter abundance
Earliest confirmation May 8 – Recently fledged young
Latest confirmation July 2 – Carrying food

Authors seem to probe a little deeper into their phrasing to describe the habitat of the Winter Wren. Fisher, hiking on Mt. St. Helena in 1900, said it "seems to delight in the spookiest corners available." Bent (1948) offered "rugged streams and romantic dells." Nesting wrens of Napa's western hills typically inhabit the larger deep, narrow redwood and fir canyons festooned in moss and fern. Logjams of stone and wooden debris are prominent habitat features. Winter Wren is a rare resident of the western hills; however, during winter it is often common in Napa Valley riparian woodland and in eastern canyons.

On May 8, 1990, fledgling Winter Wrens were discovered in the shadow of Mt. Veeder. Near the close of the Atlas, July 2, 1993, an adult carried food in Los Posadas State Forest. Nest building at Ritchey Canyon on May 23, 1989, represents a probable report, as does a pair further up Ritchey Creek in the Diamond Mt. block on May 1, 1990. Abundance was estimated at 11-100 pairs at Diamond Mt. and 2-10 pairs in the other three reporting blocks.

Historic breeding locales include those reported during the Atlas: Ritchey Canyon, Los Posadas, and Lokoya. Winter Wrens were also resident in upper Redwood Canyon into the late 1980s. Each of these sites supports Winter Wrens with diverse forest structure, where stands of old growth conifers supply the "spookiness" and the forest floor cover of downed trees and tangled debris provides shelter for the nest and young (Hejl *et al.* 2002).

MARSH WREN
Cistothorus palustris

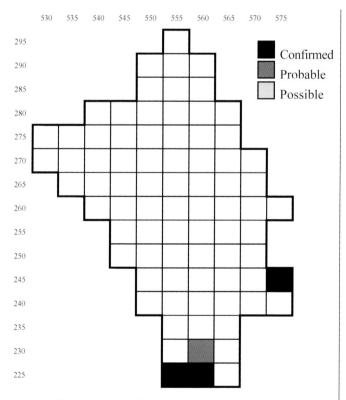

Year-round resident
Earliest confirmation June 5 – Recently fledged young
Latest confirmation June 17 – Recently fledged young

The Marsh Wren in Napa County is primarily a resident of tidal marsh. Singing males are heard throughout the year across the marsh expanse or in the brackish ditches and levee edges where the land rises toward pasture and vines. The tideland wren, *T.p. aestuarinus*, or Suisun Marsh Wren, is common in the Central Valley, and in our area its range extends north to Lake County via the "intermontane gap" of the Delta and Bay (Kroodsma and Verner 1997). At fresh-water sites, Marsh Wren nests in extensive stands of cattail and sedge. Such marshes are extremely rare in Napa County. During winter, Marsh Wren is also rare away from tidal marsh. A few can usually be found along the cattail margins of Lake Hennessey.

Fledgling Marsh Wrens were seen on June 5 and 9, 1989, in the two southwestern Atlas blocks. Territorial singing males were present in mid-June in a third tidal block. Fresh-water wrens fledged young on June 17, 1991, in a Wooden Valley marsh where several pairs were present. Abundance reports in the salt marshes ranged from as few as ten pairs at Fagan Slough to more than 100 pairs at Edgerley Island.

While not currently a species of special concern, Suisun Marsh Wren does have specific habitat needs and shares vulnerable tidal habitat with several at-risk species, including Black Rail and Common Yellowthroat. The wetland at Wooden Valley still exists, but the present status of Marsh Wren there is not known.

AMERICAN DIPPER
Cinclus mexicanus

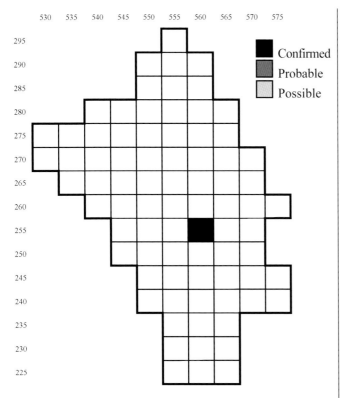

Rare year-round resident
Only confirmation May 16 – Occupied nest

Without question, the American Dipper is the least common permanent resident of the county found during the Atlas. Its habitat needs are unique; the dipper requires a clear, swift, cascading canyon stream all year. Nests are commonly placed behind a waterfall along such streams. Water temperature is important; cold water supports larger populations of invertebrates such as caddis fly and mayfly larvae, primary prey of the dipper (Bent 1948).

One breeding pair of American Dipper was found during the Atlas. On May 16, 1991, Bill Grummer, Karen Rippey and Mike Rippey located an occupied nest at Rector Falls in Rector Canyon. A nest with young found at that exact location on May 24, 1986, encouraged them to search the canyon. Since dippers' preferred nest sites are in short supply, nests are commonly placed at the same location year to year (Kingery 1996). Historical breeding records include a nest at the Chiles Mill in 1910 and a nest with young at Bell Creek's Punchbowl July 15, 1965. Swartz and Milliken Canyons are also known to have hosted dippers.

The Atlas record is the most recent report of American Dipper in Napa County. Dipper may still inhabit Rector; however, public access is restricted there, as well as in Milliken Canyon. Rector will always hold greater promise to support breeding dippers; unlike Milliken, with its reservoir above the deep canyon, Rector runs cold, deep, and wild above its reservoir, offering better foraging conditions for this unique bird.

BLUE-GRAY GNATCATCHER
Polioptila caerulea

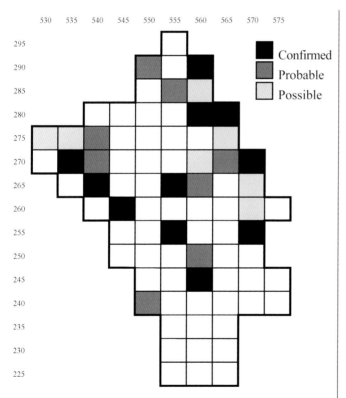

Confirmed
Probable
Possible

Summer resident
Earliest confirmation April 24 – Nest building
Latest confirmation July 27 – Recently fledged young

Almost everyone with experience with Blue-gray Gnatcatcher in Napa County considered it primarily a species of the chaparral. However, the highest densities in western North America occur in blue oak woodland (Ellison 1992), and Atlas records revealed gnatcatchers to be widespread in the extensive blue oak country of the northeastern and central parts of the county. Perhaps we may be forgiven our ignorance, since much of the prime habitat along Lake Berryessa's eastern shore was of limited access prior to the Atlas.

The earliest seasonal Atlas confirmations were, in fact, obtained in adjacent northern Berryessa blocks, where nest building was observed on April 24 and 25. Away from blue oak, nestlings were discovered in the Bothe block on May 13. Except for a south Berryessa record of an adult carrying food, the balance of confirmations involved fledglings: from May 31 at Soda Canyon through July 27 at the Palisades. Three-quarters of possible and probable data comes from May, the primary month of fieldwork throughout the Atlas. Atlasers were more reluctant than usual to report abundance; estimates came from fewer than one-third of occupied blocks. Both Soda Canyon and Cedar Roughs were estimated to support 11-100 pairs.

The Atlas found gnatcatchers locally fairly common along Napa's northeastern border and on the mixed chaparral slopes at the Palisades. The Soda Canyon population was apparently unknown previously. Prior to the Atlas, territorial gnatcatchers were reported at Skyline Park during April 1986; none was discovered there during the Atlas period.

WESTERN BLUEBIRD
Sialia mexicana

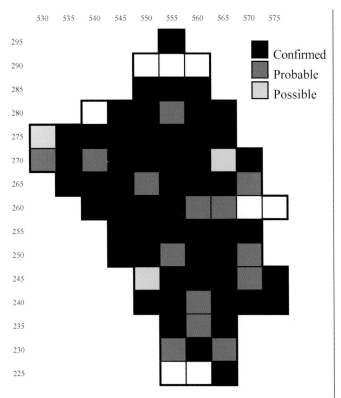

Year-round resident
Earliest confirmation April 15 – Carrying food
Latest confirmation July 31 – Feeding young

The Western Bluebird has both a conspicuous and a retiring presence. A winter flock may number in the dozens, and breeding pairs frequently pass their days at roadside fences in open country. However, pairs are quiet and often conceal themselves beyond our view in blue oak savannah or at meadows in remote chaparral. Natural cavities in living or dead trees are essential nest sites throughout their range. Bluebirds also readily occupy properly constructed and placed nest boxes. Declines of bluebirds are often due to loss of nest sites and degradation of foraging areas (Guinan *et al.* 2000).

Bluebirds were building nests in eight blocks between April 17 and May 6. Earlier nesting activity was indicated by adults carrying food for young at northeastern Lake Berryessa on April 15 and a nest with eggs on April 18 near Angwin. Nestling reports in six blocks span May 6-June 13. Fledglings were seen in 21 blocks, primarily during June, with the early and late dates at St. Helena on April 26 and August 4 at Milliken. Probable data refers to mated pairs February 26-June 30. Two successive broods raised in a nest box in St. Helena represent the lone Atlas report of possible double brooding or the use of boxes. Both are common behaviors.

Western Bluebirds remain a common species in the county. More than one-half of 39 atlasers reporting abundance estimated 11-100 pairs in their blocks. The preservation of open space, and perhaps a few nest boxes, will maintain the population.

In memory of Dorothy Marsden

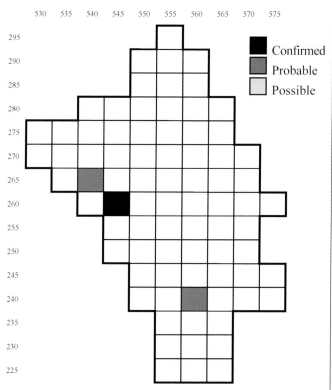

Confirmed
Probable
Possible

Summer resident
Only confirmation June 26 – Recently fledged young

The Swainson's Thrush is often the last of our breeding neotropical migrants to arrive in spring. Birds winter in mature forest from Mexico to western South America (Mack and Yong 2000) and reach Napa by the first week of May. In the lowlands, Swainson's Thrush breeds in thickets of willow and walnut. In the hills, it is found in dense cover associated with moist openings in the forest.

Swainson's Thrush has become a rare summer visitor, indeed. The three Atlas reports include territorial singing males at the Napa River south of Trancas Street June 4, 1990, and in northern Napa Valley on June 6, 1989. Fledglings were found along the Napa River at St. Helena on June 26, 1990.

Grinnell and Wythe (1927) describe Swainson's Thrush as "abundant in summer at orchards, willow-bordered streams, and forested canyons" throughout the Bay region. Through the mid-1980s, it was fairly common in extensive willow habitat along the Napa River and Conn Creek between Oakville and Yountville, and locally in upland forested Dry Creek and Redwood Canyon. Swainson's Thrush was not found in those areas during the Atlas. Alteration of lowland breeding habitat is ongoing, while several of the upland breeding areas remain intact. The peril may be hemispheric: Swainson's Thrush is one of 45 long-distance migrants most likely to be affected by tropical deforestation (Mack and Yong 2000); it is a Species of Special Concern in California.

HERMIT THRUSH
Catharus guttatus

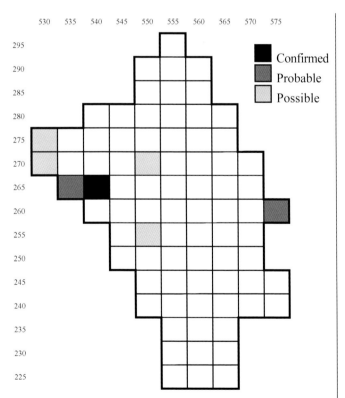

Rare summer resident, common winter resident
Only confirmation May 13 – Carrying nesting material

The Hermit Thrush passes the Napa winter in forests of every kind, broken chaparral, and backyard gardens. By the end of April most have departed for mountain forests all along the Pacific slope. Breeding birds are found in the most humid parts of the San Francisco Bay region at interior edges of coniferous forest in canyons and on north-facing slopes (Grinnell and Wythe 1927, Jones and Donovan 1996).

Hermit Thrush was found near Lake Hennessey and in two Mt. St. Helena blocks between May 1 and July 7. A singing male was near Angwin on May 23. Males were singing on territory at upper Ritchey Creek on May 4, 1990, and a bird was carrying nesting material downstream on May 13, 1989. The abundance estimate was 11-100 pairs from each of the Ritchey Creek blocks.

Prior to the Atlas, Hermit Thrush had been recorded breeding only at Bothe in June 1979. Despite the presence of similar habitat elsewhere in the county, Ritchey Canyon remains unique in sustaining a breeding population. Grinnell and Miller (1944) describe Hermit Thrush as nesting on the northeast slope of Mt. St. Helena in Lake County, as well as on Howell Mountain. Atlas records indicate that breeding may still occur at each of those historic locations.

Sponsored by Margaret Barson

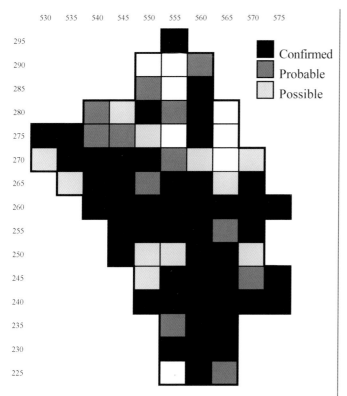

Confirmed
Probable
Possible

Year-round resident
Earliest confirmation April 4 – Nest building
Latest confirmation July 18 – Recently fledged young

Only after 1915 and the rapid increase in local gardens and other irrigated land did the American Robin become established as a breeding bird in the Bay Area (Grinnell and Miller 1944). Irrigation brought earthworms and other invertebrates to the surface and available to foraging robins (Bent 1949). Our exotic trees and shrubs are beneficial throughout the year as well, providing both food and nest sites. Historical data shows that robins probably first nested in the county in 1914 on Jefferson St. in Napa. Away from gardens and orchards, robins are found in shaded mixed forests and canyons, often far from human influence.

Eleven of the twelve Atlas nest construction records begin April 4 at Snell Valley and end at Lake Hennessey on May 6. Robins are usually double-brooded, so a bird carrying nesting material near Angwin on July 11 is not unusual. Two-thirds of 19 records of fledglings span May 15-June 23; first and last observations of fledglings are April 25 and July 18, respectively. County records which are exclusive of the Atlas and representative of later broods include nest building July 7 and 11 and nestlings July 21-August 7. Abundance estimates from 36 of the priority blocks were largely divided between 2-10 and 11-100 pairs per block.

Several priority blocks in the hot, dry northeastern interior perhaps lacked robins because of the increased intensity of the summer drought there. Elsewhere, well-watered landscaping and vineyards continue to help support this most familiar of American birds.

WRENTIT
Chamaea fasciata

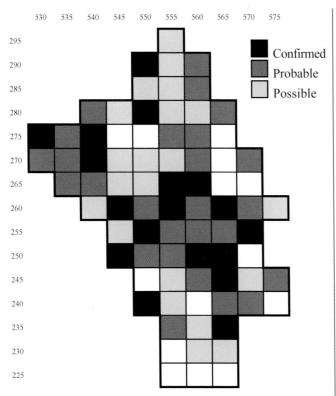

Year-round resident
Earliest confirmation May 1 – Distraction display
Latest confirmation July 18 – Recently fledged young

The Wrentit lives beneath the low canopy of chaparral. Pairs remain together through the year on a couple of acres of land. Both sexes sing, and the sound of birds from several territories becomes a quiet call and answer. Away from the chaparral, Wrentit is fairly common in lowland brush, willow, and blackberry. A few birds have crept away from native thickets into old and overgrown neighborhood gardens; such birds are often found during late summer and may represent individuals prospecting for new territories rather than established populations.

Not surprisingly, Wrentit was detected by sound in the majority of Atlas blocks. A total of 32 reports refer to singing Wrentits April 4-July 11. Considering the bird's sedentary habits, one can assume that nearly all such records represent pairs on established territories (Erickson 1948). Confirmations include nest construction above Dry Creek on May 3, nestlings southwest of Knoxville on May 19, and adults carrying food in five blocks May 2-June 6. Fledglings were near Aetna Springs on May 4, at Milliken a month later, and in eight additional blocks between June 21-July 18. Abundance was judged 11-100 pairs in 29 of the 39 reporting blocks.

The Wrentit successfully exploits almost every available brushland habitat and is found from willow thickets at Suscol Creek to ridges of chamise at the Palisades. Living in a fire-dependent ecosystem, it is resilient as well. The 1980 Atlas Peak fire incinerated nearly every bird around Rector Canyon. Within five years, Wrentit had recolonized every slope.

Sponsored by Keith and Phyllis Gish

NORTHERN MOCKINGBIRD
Mimus polyglottos

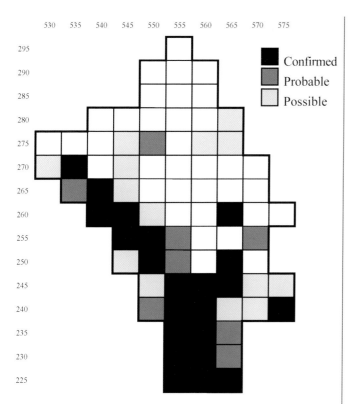

Confirmed
Probable
Possible

Year-round resident
Earliest confirmation March 16 – Carrying nesting material
Latest confirmation July 20 – Carrying food

A legendary mimic of literature and song, the Northern Mockingbird was unrecorded in the San Francisco Bay Area prior to at least 1927 (Grinnell and Wythe 1927). Mockingbirds are colonists from the deserts following the maturation of suburban shrubbery and city gardens. Grinnell and Miller referenced climate change in 1944 when they wondered if the "onset of warmer and drier climatic conditions is to some degree accountable" for the range expansion. Historical records show that Tulocay Cemetery held Napa's first nest in March 1935.

Typically raising two or three broods (Baicich and Harrison 1997), the mockingbird's lengthy season was reflected in Atlas records spanning more than four months. Birds were carrying nesting material near St. Helena on March 16 and carrying food for young southwest of Napa as late as July 20. Nest building was concentrated in April, but a July 1 record came from Gordon Valley. Most observations of active nests were during May; however, a July 8 nest was found southeast of Atlas Peak. Fledglings were seen in five blocks May 16-July 15. Not surprisingly, abundance estimates were highest around the cities of the Napa Valley.

Mockingbirds are absent across most of the upland region northeast of the Napa Valley. The scattered possible and probable records come from outposts of civilization such as Pope Valley ranches and Lake Berryessa resort communities. An expanding range of mockingbirds will follow only an increased human presence. Perhaps the mocker is one bird we'd like to see stay put.

Sponsored by Dr. William and Carlee Leftwich

CALIFORNIA THRASHER
Toxostoma redivivum

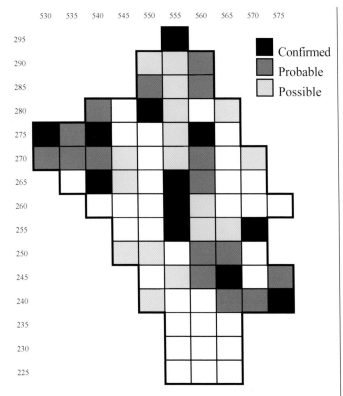

Year-round resident
Earliest confirmation April 16 – Carrying food
Latest confirmation July 18 – Recently fledged young

The California Thrasher sings throughout the year, offering an isolated counterpoint to its more common companions in chaparral, Wrentit and Bewick's Wren. The onset of winter rains triggers territorial behavior, and thrashers commonly raise two broods between February and June (Cody 1998). Away from chaparral, thrashers are less common in adjacent oak woodland and will sometimes colonize gardens where a mosaic of native and exotic vegetation provides habitat.

The median egg date north of Santa Cruz County is April 20 ± 32 days (Cody 1998). During the Atlas, thrashers were observed carrying food for young south of Lake Hennessey by April 16 and as late as June 18 at Milliken. Fledged young were reported May 27 at Bothe and in six additional blocks June 30-July 18. Records of pairs and singing males include three March observations. Atlasers were not in the field during the early part of the nesting season. Data from Alta Heights between 1979-1988 includes two Feb. 16 nest building records, a March 11 occupied nest, and a March 28 nest with eggs.

California Thrasher is locally common, primarily in chaparral, from Knoxville south and east to Lake Curry, and across the Palisades to Mt. St. Helena. Thrashers are vulnerable to habitat fragmentation, however, and are one of the first species lost in remnant patches of developed chaparral (Cody 1998). The Atlas did not determine the extent to which thrashers inhabit backyard gardens; considering house cat and Western Scrub-Jay predation (pers. obs.), it is probably insignificant.

138

EUROPEAN STARLING
Sturnus vulgaris

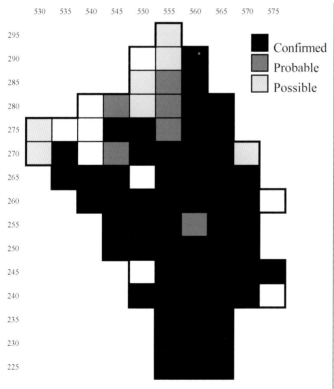

	Confirmed
	Probable
	Possible

Year-round resident
Earliest confirmation April 6 – Carrying nesting material
Latest confirmation September 7 – Occupied nest

The European Starling is believed to have arrived in Califorma in January 1942 (Bent 1950) and has since found Napa County a welcome home. Tens of thousands forage in vineyards in late fall, and early winter roosts at the Napa River Ecological Reserve have exceeded one-quarter million individuals. It nests in a variety of habitats, finding a cavity in which to raise its young among the concrete and steel of industry or in an ancient valley oak. It usurps the breeding sites of native cavity nesters.

Nest building reports include April 6 at Jamieson Canyon and June 2 at Coombsville. Ten occupied nests were found April 7-July 7. Nestlings at four locations span May 7-12; a Carneros report is dated June 30. Adults carried food for young in 14 blocks April 26-May 16 and in two June 26 and July 3. Parents tended fledglings in 14 blocks May 11-June 19. Eighty-one percent of the 57 total confirmations span April 22-June 11. Abundance estimates exceeding 100 pairs came from eight scattered blocks. The high elevations of Mt. St. Helena and the Palisades have few breeding starlings. The remote hills south of Knoxville support a marginal population.

European Starling may be declining. Angwin Christmas Bird Count totals for European Starling exceeded 10,000 in six counts, 1986-1992. Excepting 53,000 in 1996, the total has not exceeded 6400 since 1993 (www.audubon.org/bird/cbc). However, a reduced early winter presence may correspond only to a reduction in waste grapes available and not to a declining breeding population.

PHAINOPEPLA
Phainopepla nitens

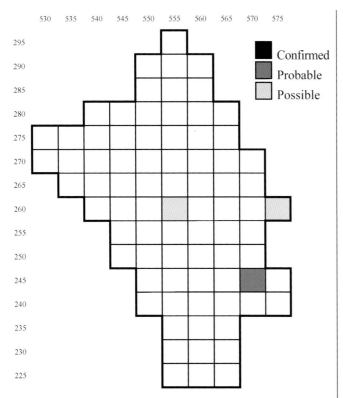

Rare spring visitor, rare early winter visitor
Only probable May 7 – Visiting probable nest site

There remains a great deal to learn about the breeding biology of Phainopepla in California. It has two distinct breeding seasons: in desert areas during late winter, and in the central foothills in late spring. Chu and Walsberg (1999) describe three theories regarding Phainopepla behavior. In the dual-breeding hypothesis, the same individuals breed annually in both the south and the north with about 30 days separating the two seasons. The two-population hypothesis suggests that these are two separate populations breeding at different times of the year. And in the failed-breeding hypothesis, unsuccessful desert breeders travel north and try again. Phainopepla in our area is found in dry live oak-chaparral and riparian woodland (Chu and Walsberg 1999). The presence of fruit, especially mistletoe, is a common habitat feature.

Atlas records include an individual in the Monticello Dam block on May 10, 1990, and an adult male in Chiles Valley on July 2, 1993. A bird was visiting a probable nest site just west of Lake Curry on May 7, 1990.

Phainopepla has yet to be confirmed breeding in Napa County. On occasion during early winter, the species is found on the Angwin Christmas Bird Count; summer observations remain rare and unrevealing.

ORANGE-CROWNED WARBLER
Vermivora celata

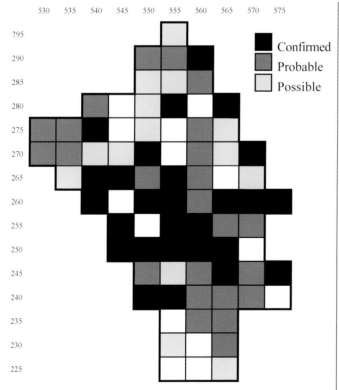

| Confirmed |
| Probable |
| Possible |

Summer resident
Earliest confirmation April 20 – Carrying food
Latest confirmation July 28 – Feeding young

Orange-crowned Warbler is the first neotropical migrant to return to breeding areas early each year, excepting perhaps several swallow species. Singing males are usually heard beginning around Mar. 1. By the end of March territories are established in habitats that include chaparral, riparian tangles, and the brushy edges of mixed upland forests.

Nest building April 20 at Monticello Dam and nestlings at Bothe April 26 are the only such reports. The eight reports of adults carrying food for young range from April 20 at Milliken through June 20 east of Lake Berryessa. Sixteen blocks held fledglings May 8-July 3. Orange-crowneds are single-brooded but will re-nest. The average date of nestlings in second attempts is June 2 (Sogge *et al.* 1994). A report of fledglings near St. Helena July 28 falls outside the known breeding season. Approximately two-thirds of confirmed and probable data spans May 15-June 15. The June 21, 1993, record of an adult feeding a fledgling Brown-headed Cowbird at southwestern Lake Berryessa is interesting. Cowbird parasitism of this warbler in the United States was not reported in Sogge *et al.* (1994), and W.T. Gilbert (pers. comm.) did not record parasitism during a ten-year study in the Berkeley Hills. However, three historical records of Orange-crowned Warbler feeding fledgling cowbirds June 10-30 between 1982 and 1988 do exist from the Napa River at Oakville and Yountville.

Orange-crowned Warblers breed in suitable habitat throughout the county, absent only from tidal marsh, agricultural areas, hard chaparral such as chamise, and oak savannah.

YELLOW WARBLER
Dendroica petechia

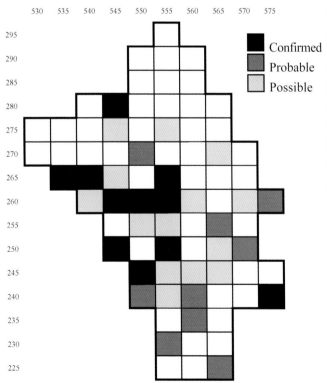

Confirmed
Probable
Possible

Summer resident
Earliest confirmation April 30 – Nest building
Latest confirmation July 28 – Nest with young

As is the case with many species that join us in spring, the Yellow Warbler usually makes its appearance without preliminaries as a singing male on its breeding territory. In Napa County it is usually singing from a willow-bordered stream or pond. Oaks or alders might make up part of the overstory of trees, but willows define the breeding habitat. Lengthy stretches of a stream are favored; however, small patches of willow where small creeks empty into reservoirs also support nesting pairs.

Yellow Warbler arrives in Napa April 10-15. Nest construction was observed in three blocks between April 30 at Gordon Valley and May 25 at Conn Valley. Adults carrying food were at Redwood Creek on May 12 and in three additional blocks June 13-28. There was an occupied nest at Yountville June 19 and nestlings at Larkmead on July 28. Fledglings were in Chiles Valley May 28 and near Rutherford June 15. Reports of probable nesting birds span April 30-June 13.

In recent years Yellow Warbler has disappeared from parts of its former breeding range, including Mill and Ritchey Creeks located up the Napa Valley. The Valley represents about one-third of its current distribution and includes several marginal sites, such as Napa Creek in the city of Napa. Habitat at many locations is limited to isolated patches of willows: the feeder streams of Lake Hennessey, Dry Creek Canyon, and Redwood Canyon. Because of habitat loss, Yellow Warbler is a Species of Special Concern in California.

Sponsored by Vernon Gross in memory of Marguerite Gross

YELLOW-RUMPED WARBLER
Dendroica coronata

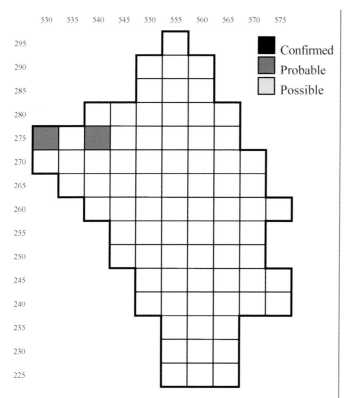

Confirmed
Probable
Possible

Rare summer resident, common winter resident
Earliest probable May 10 – Pair observed
Latest probable May 12 – Pair observed

The Yellow-rumped Warbler is an abundant winter bird in lowlands; during April and May it moves into mountainous terrain to breed. It is a common migrant here throughout the month of April, and a very few are found during the Napa summer, exclusively in Douglas fir forests above 2000 feet elevation. There are two historical breeding records in the county: June 15, 1932, on Mt. Veeder; and June 21, 1972, west of Aetna Springs. Three additional June records involve singing males on the east side of Sugarloaf Mt. along Aetna Springs Road. Birds were found June 23-30 in three years during the 1980s in open stands of Douglas fir on precipitous slopes.

One of the two Atlas reports comes from the block that includes the historic Aetna Springs observations. Atlasers found a mated pair there on May 12, 1991. On Mt. St. Helena, observers discovered a pair on May 10, 1992. They estimated an abundance of 2-10 pairs in the block.

At present, Yellow-rumped Warbler is not known to nest in Napa County. It is perhaps a regular summer resident at Sugarloaf and St. Helena. Repeated visits to these mountains by a persistent observer, especially during the month of June, might once again discover a nesting pair.

BLACK-THROATED GRAY WARBLER
Dendroica nigrescens

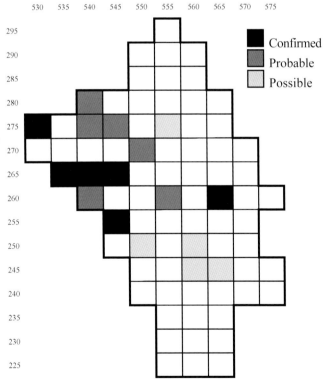

Summer resident
Earliest confirmation April 27 – Carrying nesting material
Latest confirmation July 6 – Recently fledged young

Confirmed
Probable
Possible

Reaching Napa around April 10, Black-throated Gray Warblers migrate along foothill ridges through early May. Breeding birds are generally limited to areas at higher elevations with diverse tree and shrub species. Associations of interior live oak, Sargent cypress, manzanita, and mountain mahogany interspersed with Douglas fir or knobcone pine provide primary nesting habitat (Dunn and Garrett 1997). Breeding sites are remote; however, fall migrants are common on the Napa Valley floor, affording anyone a glimpse of this beautiful warbler.

Even as migration continued, summer residents were seen carrying nesting material southwest of Calistoga on April 27. Territorial individuals, pairs, and singing males were found in four additional northwestern blocks April 26-May 9. Fledglings were at Bothe June 15 and southwest of St. Helena July 6. Adults with fledglings were near Angwin June 28 and on the western slope of Mt. St. Helena on June 30. An outlying pair was feeding young above Capell Creek July 3. Records of possible breeding birds on May 8-25 at Soda Canyon, Milliken Canyon, and Oakville Grade are in areas where the warbler was unknown as a nesting species.

On May 12, 1939, a nest with eggs was found within a mile east of Angwin. Howell Mt., Swartz Canyon, and the Palisades remain the species' core range. Much of this land is protected through association with The Land Trust of Napa County, and by Robert Louis Stevenson State Park and other public holdings.

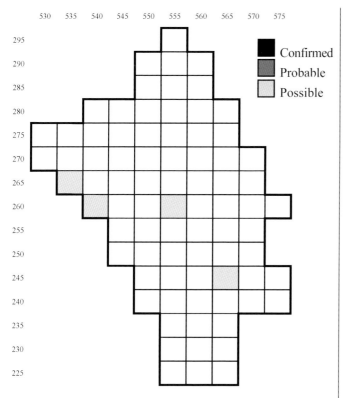

Confirmed
Probable
Possible

Rare summer resident
Earliest possible April 29 – Singing male in habitat
Latest possible July 3 – Species in habitat

Over 50 years have passed since a MacGillivray's Warbler was discovered attending young at Lokoya Lodge on June 10, 1949. Since that day there have been fewer than ten records during the nesting season. MacGillivray's Warblers in the northern Coast Ranges inhabit dense thickets in shaded canyons and streams (Grinnell and Miller 1944), and "tangles adjacent to oak woodland and riparian associations" (Dunn and Garrett 1997). MacGillivray's Warbler is most easily seen in the county during August and September, when migrants are found in lowland riparian thickets.

During the Atlas period, individual MacGillivray's Warblers were found in suitable nesting habitat on May 29, 1993, and July 3, 1989, at adjacent blocks in the northwest. A male was discovered northeast of Lake Hennessey April 29, 1990, and an individual was in the Milliken Canyon block May 20, 1991. Complete egg clutches are known in California April 28-July 10 (Pitocchelli 1995); therefore, each Atlas record could represent breeding birds. However, spring migrants occur at non-breeding locales April 23-May, complicating the status of early reports.

At least four other summer records precede the Atlas: individuals at the Rutherford Quarry July 15, 1962, at Van Ness Creek June 23, 1988, and two of Napa's oldest breeding records – eggs and young in two nests near Napa Creek in June 1859. MacGillivray's Warbler becomes common in the Coast Range from Mendocino County northward (Grinnell and Miller 1944). Nearest to Napa, small numbers summer along Ida Clayton Road on Mt. St. Helena's northwestern slope.

COMMON YELLOWTHROAT
Geothlypis trichas

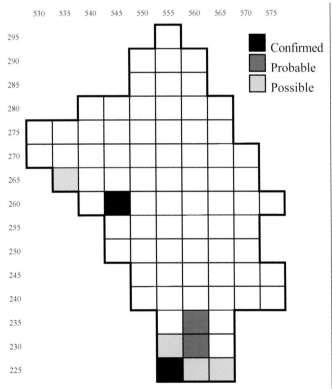

Confirmed
Probable
Possible

Year-round resident
Earliest confirmation May 27 – Carrying food
Latest confirmation June 11 – Recently fledged young

Two distinctive subspecies of Common Yellowthroat are found in Napa County. The "Saltmarsh" Yellowthroat, *G.t. sinuosa*, is a resident of the tidal marsh system from Kennedy Park southward. Its San Francisco Bay population declined 80-95 percent during the 20th century (Guzy and Ritchison 1999), concurrent with a similar reduction in its tidal habitat (PRBO Conservation Science 1999). *G.t. arizela*, which inhabits wet riparian thickets and fresh-water marshes, is a common spring and fall migrant, and a rare summer visitor. Its historic breeding status is uncertain; there is a May 22, 1948, nest record "three miles north of Napa" along the river, and adult males were seen May 16-July 15 during four different years, 1981-1988, at the Napa River Ecological Reserve.

Common Yellowthroat was found in each of the six Atlas priority blocks touching on tidal marsh. Singing males were recorded in five blocks February 24-May 9. An adult was carrying food for young on Coon Island on May 27, 1993, where the local population was described as "quite thick." The fresh-water yellowthroat was found near Calistoga on June 4, 1991, and at St. Helena a week later, where fledglings were observed.

There is apparently insufficient lowland habitat in the Napa Valley to sustain a population of *G.t. arizela*, and its occurrence remains irregular. The "Saltmarsh" Yellowthroat is relatively common in intact tidal marsh; however, its habitat is limited and vulnerable. It is currently a Species of Special Concern in California, as well as a candidate for Federal Endangered status.

WILSON'S WARBLER
Wilsonia pusilla

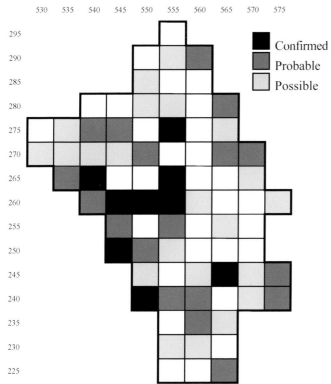

	Confirmed
	Probable
	Possible

Summer resident
Earliest confirmation April 12 – Carrying nesting material
Latest confirmation July 14 – Carrying food

The Wilson's Warbler is a voice in the dappled light of the undergrowth, its presence a sign of moisture at the onset of the summer drought. Singing males defend territories beginning the first week of April. Upland habitats are characterized by a dense understory, often at blow-downs or clear-cuts (Dunn and Garrett 1997) in mixed forests or at the edge of similar openings. Riparian woodland, especially where dense willow shades tangled shrubs, is equally acceptable.

Fieldwork produced two nest construction records: Conn Valley April 12, and Pope Canyon April 28. A long-term Contra Costa County study revealed a mean nest building date of April 17 (Ammon and Gilbert 1999). Adults were carrying food for young at Chiles Creek May 22 and at Milliken July 14. Fledglings were detected at five locations, including the early record at Redwood Canyon May 30, and late along Dry Creek July 5. About 20 percent of females in Marin Co. produce second broods, and all females in Contra Costa Co. re-nest if the first clutch is lost (Ammon and Gilbert 1999). Atlas records in July probably represent such behavior. Possible nesting data describes singing males in 14 blocks April 18-June 13. Probable reports, primarily pairs and singing males, span April 15-June 22.

Wilson's Warbler is common in the canyons and mixed forests of the western hills from Hogback Ridge north to Diamond Mt. Elsewhere it is more patchily distributed, and densities are low. Wilson's Warbler will benefit from the protection and restoration of valley riparian woodland.

YELLOW-BREASTED CHAT
Icteria virens

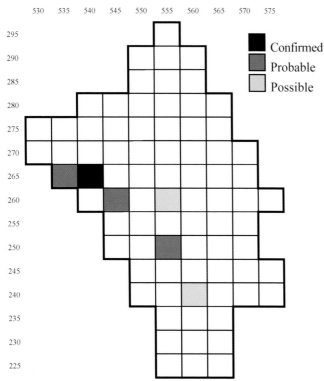

Summer resident
Only confirmation May 29 – Feeding young

Confirmed
Probable
Possible

In the old days at Napa River Ecological Reserve, a glorious display of avian chaos and song occurred in late April as newly arrived male Yellow-breasted Chats competed for choice territories along Conn Creek. Dense thickets of willow, blackberry, and wild grape supported up to ten pairs each year. Elsewhere, remnant well-vegetated stretches of the Napa River and its lowland tributaries held scattered breeding pairs from Napa to Calistoga.

Chats were found at five locations the length of the Napa Valley during four Atlas years. Territorial males sang along the Napa River near Calistoga, St. Helena, and Yountville June 1-20. A silent individual was on the northeastern outskirts of Napa June 7; a singing male in Chiles Valley May 6, 1990, represents the lone observation away from the Napa Valley. Chats fed fledglings in blackberry thickets along the river at Larkmead May 29, 1989. Historical Napa Valley records refer primarily to observations of fledglings June 13-August 17.

The "old days" at the Napa River Ecological Reserve were the 1980s. At present, anecdotal evidence suggests that Yellow-breasted Chat has all but vanished from the Napa Valley. Recent historical breeding habitat has either been destroyed or too severely narrowed by encroaching vineyards and development. Reduced genetic diversity at the increasingly isolated Napa River Ecological Reserve may doom that population. Breeding Bird Survey evidence of a stable population in California is weakened by low numbers of birds per survey route (Sauer *et al.* 2002). Yellow-breasted Chat is a Species of Special Concern in California.

WESTERN TANAGER
Piranga ludoviciana

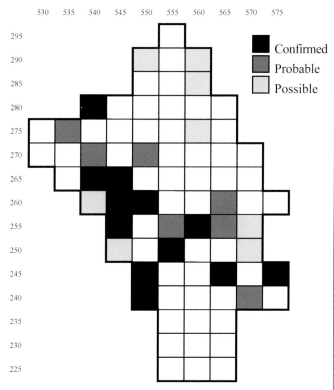

Confirmed
Probable
Possible

Summer resident, rare winter resident
Earliest confirmation May 21 – Carrying food
Latest confirmation July 5 – Recently fledged young

Although brightly colored, the Western Tanager is at times a reluctant singer and is often difficult to detect within the forest canopy during the nesting season. Tanagers favor the moist mixed forests in the hills above the Napa Valley, as well as groves of live oak along the river. They are common during spring, arriving about April 20, and migrants are widespread in a variety of habitats well into May. Western Tanagers are fond of fruit and are often seen during July at ripening wild plums the length of the Valley.

The nesting season begins after the middle of May, and mated pairs and singing males were seen in six blocks through June 13. Tanagers were building nests near Bothe May 26 and on the slopes of Mt. Veeder June 14. Adults carried food for young near St. Helena on June 6 and southeast of Atlas Peak on June 18. Fledglings were first seen near Angwin June 9; six additional records span June 26-July 5. Abundance reports of 2-10 pairs were consistent throughout the county.

Grinnell and Miller (1944) reported Western Tanager breeding "near sea level, as at Napa." Habitat may be limited around the city today, but tanagers are still found in selected parts of the Valley where live oak and riparian vegetation remains. The conservation of even small groves of oak can be beneficial. Project Tanager, a Cornell University study, found that Western Tanager is almost as likely to breed in small patches of oak as in large ones.

Sponsored by Jerry and Theresa Karr

SPOTTED TOWHEE
Pipilo maculatus

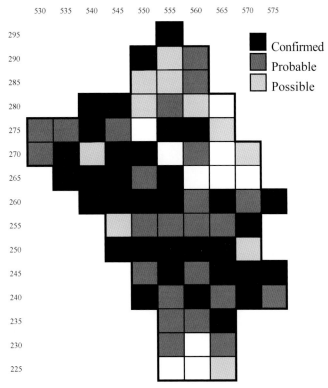

	Confirmed
	Probable
	Possible

Year-round resident
Earliest confirmation March 27 – Carrying nesting material
Latest confirmation July 23 – Feeding young

Among birds on the ground and out of sight, the Spotted Towhee is the most widespread, if not the most common of them all. It is found in lowland riparian thickets; in shrubby tangles at the edges of mixed forests in the hills and canyons; in most types of chaparral; and in gardens where brush is allowed to flourish. A well-developed litter and humus layer beneath a closed shrub canopy is an ideal foraging environment for this towhee (Greenlaw 1996). It frequently raises two and sometimes three broods.

Atlas data reflects the extended and often prolific season. Extremes are illustrated by observations of adults carrying nesting material southeast of Atlas Peak on March 27 and at Redwood Canyon on July 18. Eggs were found at Deer Park May 1 and a nest with young at St. Helena April 26. Records of fledglings may represent the timing of first and second broods; seven such records span May 16-June 5, while 12 range between June 17-July 23. Historical records reflecting the extended season include nests with young May 10, 1981, and August 6, 1987, at the Napa River Ecological Reserve.

It is not surprising that Spotted Towhee was absent from the tidal marshes of the south and the open shores and oak savannah east of Lake Berryessa. Its absence from the Cedar Roughs and weak evidence on the serpentine soils south of Knoxville may be attributable to relatively thin humus and leaf litter development found locally in cypress, foothill pine and chaparral habitat.

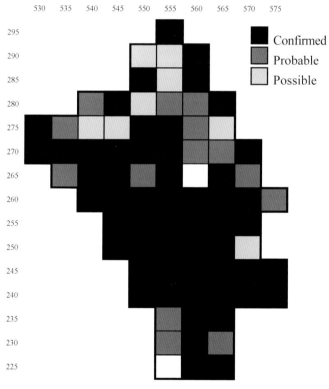

| | Confirmed |
| Probable |
| Possible |

Year-round resident
Earliest confirmation March 15 – Nest building
Latest confirmation July 12 – Carrying food

The California Towhee in your yard isn't going very far. A sedentary bird, once mated it is hopelessly devoted to the small brushy territory it has established. Towhees are natives of chaparral hillsides, riparian thickets, and more open oak-foothill pine woodland. Towhees have found our gardens particularly inviting. In fact, the disordered nature of some residential areas supports towhees in greater densities than in the more uniform native habitat (Childs 1968). The long nesting season can extend into September, and a pair may raise up to four broods (Baicich and Harrison 1997).

The first of nine Atlas-period nest construction efforts was reported from northwestern Napa on March 15 and the last at Mt. St. Helena on June 16. Nests with eggs were discovered in Calistoga on May 17 and Knoxville June 21. There were four reports of nestlings April 26-June 30. The 11 records of adults carrying food for young span April 18-July 12. Fledglings were seen in 24 blocks May 2-July 7. Abundance estimates tended highest in low-density rural residential areas such as Coombsville and lowest across unbroken blocks of chaparral such as the Cedar Roughs.

Despite being a bird "with no bright colors, no attractive song and no tricks or manners of especial interest" (Hoffman 1927), the California Towhee is a bird of great appeal. It leads a fascinating life of song, courtship, territorial defense and reproduction right outside the door and is not especially secretive in these behaviors. Towhees offer us the opportunity to learn.

RUFOUS-CROWNED SPARROW
Aimophila ruficeps

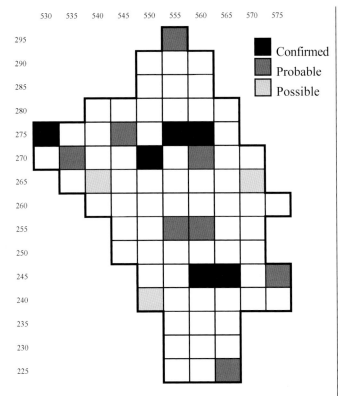

Year-round resident
Earliest confirmation May 31 – Recently fledged young
Latest confirmation July 18 – Recently fledged young

The Rufous-crowned Sparrow is a resident in selected parts of the county. It is essentially a bird of the chaparral but favors the sort with a greater diversity of vegetation, including scattered small oaks and areas of open grass, usually with assorted rock outcroppings. There is sometimes a little shift during winter onto open grassy slopes, but mated pairs (Collins 1999) generally remain on breeding territories through the winter.

Rufous-crowned Sparrow was found nesting in three relatively small areas: Atlas Peak, Putah Creek, and Mt. St. Helena. Atlas Peak area confirmations included fledglings and adults carrying food at Soda and Milliken Canyons around Memorial Day. Fledglings were seen at Putah Creek on July 12 and 18 and to the west above Pope Valley on the July 5. Very exciting was the discovery of a nest with eggs on Mt. St. Helena July 1.

The specialized habitat of Rufous-crowned Sparrow is, in general, remote and difficult to access. Much of its range is on protected land such as the Milliken and Rector watersheds, Land Trust of Napa County conservation easements including an Atlas Peak ranch and Sutro Surber, and the patchwork public holdings around Knoxville and Putah Creek. The species can be vulnerable, however. The widespread subspecies of southern California, *A.r. canescens*, is a Species of Special Concern in the state and was considered for federal threatened or endangered status. Locally, fire suppression may adversely affect habitat quality by creating dense stands of "decadent" chaparral (Collins 1999).

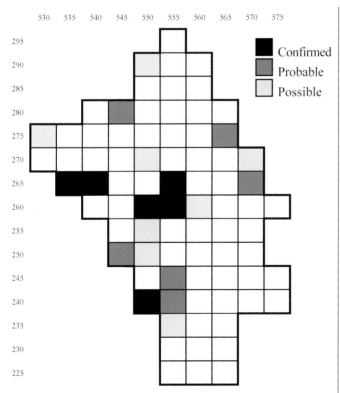

Year-round resident
Earliest confirmation May 24 – Carrying food
Latest confirmation July 6 – Feeding young

Western Chipping Sparrows, unlike the continent's eastern population, tend to favor more natural habitats somewhat removed from human habitation. A variety of open forest types with at most a grassy understory is preferred (Johnson 1968). In the Napa Valley this is often represented by large, spreading live oaks that allow meager ground cover. "Chippies" arrive in the Valley the end of March, with territorial behavior often evident by the middle of April.

However, during the Atlas period the earliest evidence of summer residency was that of pairs found in two blocks on the eastern shore of Lake Berryessa May 2 and 3, 1992. April records are limited to individuals in two blocks during the third week of the month. Adults were carrying food for young in Conn Valley May 24 and in Redwood Canyon a month later. Fledglings were found near Los Posadas and Chiles Valley on June 11 and at two northern Napa Valley sites June 20 and July 6. Probable records of pairs, apart from the early Berryessa records, span May 24–June 13.

Chipping Sparrow is an uncommon and randomly distributed breeding species in the county. Atlas results suggest that these sparrows favor valley sites and perhaps oak savannah. The abundance estimate at five of the confirmed blocks was ten or fewer pairs. One Bothe block was judged to support 11-100 pairs. Grinnell and Miller (1944) describe orchards as a favored habitat in California. Perhaps Chipping Sparrow was more numerous when the county's fruit production was more diverse.

LARK SPARROW
Chondestes grammacus

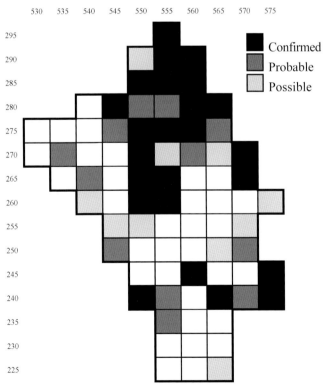

Year-round resident
Earliest confirmation April 5 – Carrying nesting material
Latest confirmation July 31 – Carrying food

The Lark Sparrow differs from the rest of our flocking winter sparrows in two respects: winter flocks usually contain only Lark Sparrows, and many remain in the county to nest. Winter flocks may be elusive and wandering but breeding birds are reliable. Lark Sparrows are found in dry, open, wooded or shrubby situations, including blue oak woodland, foothill pine, broken chaparral, and rocky meadows with few woody plants. Poor soil supporting minimal herbaceous vegetation is a common habitat feature.

Lark Sparrows were building nests on April 5 southeast of Angwin, April 9 at both Lake Curry and Partrick Road, and in five additional blocks May 2-June 23. Nests with eggs were found in the four county line blocks between Knoxville and Lake Berryessa: three in 1990 between May 1-June 25, and one on May 16, 1993. Adults carrying food for young were seen in the two blocks south of Knoxville on May 9, on July 18 in Pope Canyon and in Gordon Valley July 31. Five records of fledglings span May 31-July 7. Probable data refers primarily to mated pairs April 20-June 28. Reports from 19 of 23 blocks estimated an abundance of 2-10 pairs, an unusually consistent trend for any species during the Atlas.

The Lark Sparrow is widespread across the northeastern foothills where open blue oak woodland and mixed pine-chaparral are the dominant habitats. It is an uncommon breeding bird wherever it is found, apparently occurring in naturally low densities.

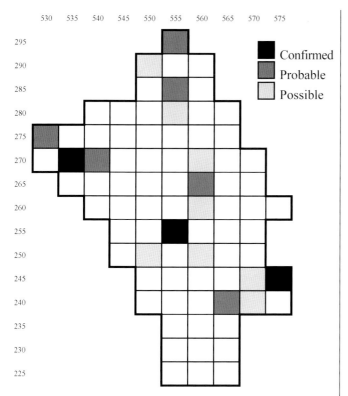

Confirmed
Probable
Possible

Year-round resident
Earliest confirmation June 8 – Carrying food
Latest confirmation July 27 – Recently fledged young

One of the most difficult resident birds of Napa County to find and see may be the Sage Sparrow. Grinnell and Miller (1944) describe its habitat as "chaparral of arid, or 'hard' type, usually fairly dense or continuous." Oat Hill Mine Road is an excellent area that offers both that habitat and the sparrow. Farther south, Sage Sparrow frequents less dense chaparral of greater plant diversity, commonly where patches of exposed bedrock allow little except grasses to grow. Across the broad area of Rector and Milliken Canyons, Sage Sparrow prefers more level ridge and flat tableland chaparral.

Sage Sparrow was confirmed breeding in three blocks during 1991. Adults were carrying food north of Rector Canyon on June 8, while recently fledged young were at Lake Curry on June 29 and at the Palisades on July 27. Probable records during the Atlas period describe pairs in five blocks April 14-May 21, and a territorial singing male at Knoxville on June 27. Possible data includes singing males found on one day only in five blocks May 10-July 5. Abundance estimates of 11-100 pairs came from east of Wild Horse Valley, upper Putah Creek, and the Cedar Roughs.

Sage Sparrow is locally common. However, it is erratically distributed across the county's expanses of chaparral, and to state that it is a "chaparral species" is an oversimplification. Its habitat requirements are more refined than that, and at present we understand those refinements only a little.

SAVANNAH SPARROW
Passerculus sandwichensis

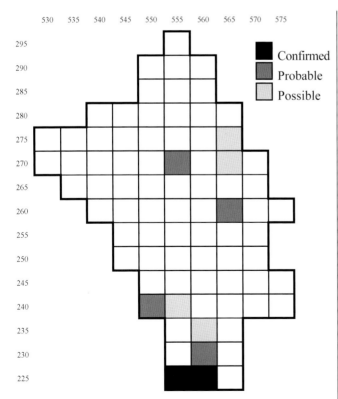

Year-round resident
Earliest confirmation May 26 – Nest building
Latest confirmation June 15 – Carrying food

Away from the southwestern edge of the county, Savannah Sparrow is a rare summer presence, indeed. But at the grassland margins of the tidal marshes, it is one of the most common nesting songbirds. Grazed pastures adjacent to the Napa River below the city of Napa support fewer birds. Further inland, Savannah Sparrows are found in grasslands at Pope Valley and Lake Berryessa.

There were two confirmations during the Atlas period. On June 15, 1989, an adult was carrying food near Edgerley Island, and on May 26, 1991, a bird was discovered building a nest near the county airport. April observations of pairs at southeastern Pope Valley and along Partrick Road represent probable records. A pair was found in early June at the southwestern shore of Lake Berryessa. During May a singing male was present along the Napa River immediately south of the city of Napa. Additional reports include two blocks adjacent to Napa and the two eastern Lake Berryessa blocks where the open shore may support a few pairs of nesting sparrows. Abundance was reported from the three southern blocks, with 10-100 in two, and 100-1000 pairs present near Edgerley Island.

The Edgerley Island block includes the Huichica Creek Wildlife Area, which at present supports most of the county's breeding population. Pastures east of the Napa County Airport once held a small number of birds throughout the summer but are now developed. Savannah Sparrow may benefit in the future from grasslands restored as part of the Napa River flood management and restoration project.

GRASSHOPPER SPARROW
Ammodramus savannarum

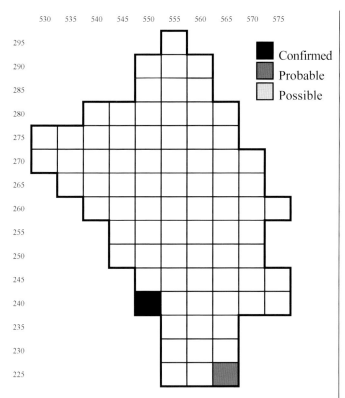

Confirmed
Probable
Possible

Rare summer resident
Only confirmation May 7 – Carrying food

Napa County's first records of Grasshopper Sparrow were those discovered during the Atlas. It is a rare and locally distributed breeding bird in the North Bay counties, and site fidelity is low. In a California study, only 20 percent of successful breeding males returned to the same location the following year (Vickery 1996). It is found in dry, well-drained grassland where the presence of a diversity of plant species is often more important than the specific plant types (Grinnell and Miller 1944).

Three or four singing males, found in an ungrazed portion of a ranch in Jamieson Canyon April 13-27, 1989, represent the first Napa County record of Grasshopper Sparrow. No birds were seen after April 27. Between May 5-11, 1990, Peggy Gross and Nicholas Biehle monitored the county's first nesting pair on the grassy slopes along Partrick Road. An adult was observed carrying food there on May 7 and 8.

The habitat at each of the Atlas observations was the ungrazed, uncultivated upland typical of open grassland throughout Napa County. This habitat remains relatively common, especially in the southeast. Conditions favored Grasshopper Sparrow on Partrick Road until at least 1997. Up to seven singing males were present during May 1994. There is one winter record, February 16, 1997, at the Napa Airport.

SONG SPARROW
Melospiza melodia

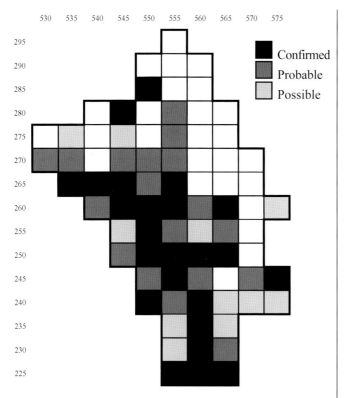

Year-round resident
Earliest confirmation March 14 – Carrying nesting material
Latest confirmation August 20 – Feeding young

Two subspecies of Song Sparrow are Napa County residents. *M.m. gouldii*, Marin Song Sparrow, inhabits Napa Valley stream-side and moist thickets; it is rare in canyons and foothill springs. *M.m. samuelis*, Samuel's Song Sparrow, resides only in tidal marsh and is one of three unique forms of Song Sparrow living in San Francisco Bay marshes. Samuel's favors marsh shrub cover and is most common where gumplant and coyote brush are found; densities are greatest in large, contiguous marsh (Nur and Spautz 2002). The divide between populations of *samuelis* and *gouldii* is marked; *gouldii* is the subspecies where fresh-water vegetation begins, 1.2 miles south of Napa (Marshall 1948).

Mated pairs and territorial singing male Marin Song Sparrows were found March 17-July 4. Nest construction was noted at Jamieson Canyon March 14 and St. Helena April 23. Nestlings were seen southeast of Atlas Peak May 15. Adults carried food for young in seven blocks May 2-July 2. Fledglings were described from 11 locations between May 16 at Yountville and August 20 at upper Putah Creek. Confirmations of *samuelis* can only be inferred; the three tidal marsh blocks also support *gouldii*, and the data do not describe subspecies.

The total San Pablo Bay population of Samuel's Song Sparrow is an estimated 70,000-85,000 (Nur and Spautz 2002). It lives in dangerously isolated, vulnerable habitat where predation is chiefly responsible for low reproductive success; fewer than 20 percent of nests fledge at least one young (Spautz 2002). It is a Species of Special Concern in California.

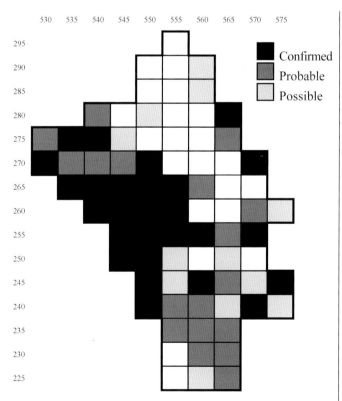

Year-round resident
Earliest confirmation March 11 – Carrying nesting material
Latest confirmation August 3 – Recently fledged young

Late in winter, the flocks of Dark-eyed Junco disperse throughout the forested hills to nest. A few juncos breed in the lowlands, but most are found from the lowest hills around the city of Napa up to the mountains at the head of the Napa Valley. Dark-eyed Junco is common in moist mixed conifer and oak-madrone forests, where nests are often near fire roads or similar edgy openings. Juncos are also found in dry, relatively dense mixed oak woodlands. In both primary habitats, a well-developed ground layer of herbaceous vegetation is important (Phelps 1968). A fallen branch or an earthen ledge frequently shelters ground nests.

A Dark-eyed Junco along Spring Mountain Rd. was carrying nesting material on March 11. Occupied nests were found in three blocks April 26-June 14, and adults were carrying food for young in four blocks April 22-May 7. Fledglings were found in 19 blocks May 2-August 3; 15 such records span May-June. Probable reports refer to pairs and singing males, primarily during May and June.

Dark-eyed Junco is most common in the moist conifer belt from Redwood Canyon, north to Los Posadas and west to Calistoga. Its absence from a large part of the northeastern interior is habitat-related. Serpentine soils, steep slopes, and chaparral do not support the relatively dense ground vegetation that nesting juncos require.

BLACK-HEADED GROSBEAK
Pheucticus melanocephalus

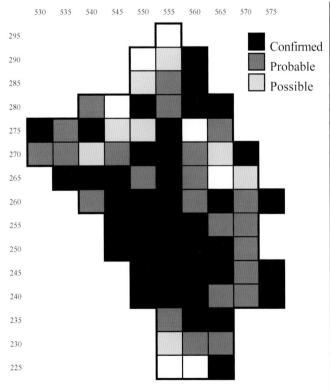

Confirmed
Probable
Possible

Summer resident
Earliest confirmation April 9 – Nest building
Latest confirmation August 8 – Feeding young

Black-headed Grosbeak arrives in Napa during the first week of April, and, by the 20th, endlessly caroling males are competing for territories throughout the county. Lowland streams, wooded canyons, and mixed upland forests appear to support grosbeaks equally. Grinnell and Miller (1944) believed that diversity of plant growth and extensive edge conditions were important factors in all grosbeak habitats. Given sufficient cover, they will nest in backyard gardens (Hill 1995).

In California the median date of 543 completed clutches is May 23; second broods are unknown, and eggs after June 1 are believed to be re-nests (Hill 1995). During the Atlas, early nest building was observed at Monticello Dam on Apr. 9 and at Bothe Apr. 12; May 14 is the last of the four reports. Nests with young were found above Aetna Springs on May 4 and at Spencer Creek on May 25; three occupied nests were discovered May 15-20. Reports of fledglings or adults feeding fledglings in 25 blocks span May 16-Aug. 8 (median date = June 14). The August 8 observation of adults attending fledglings in Jamieson Canyon is the extreme of the season. A majority of probable records involve singing males or pairs in early May to mid-June.

The small gaps in a county-wide distribution are clearly habitat related. Black-headed Grosbeaks avoid oak savannah and hard chaparral around Pope Valley and in a few northern border blocks. Stream corridors probably support most of the grosbeaks in more arid interior areas where upland habitat lacks diversity.

LAZULI BUNTING
Passerina amoena

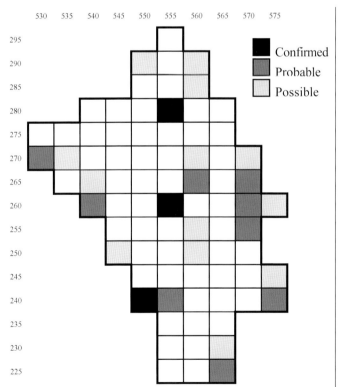

530	535	540	545	550	555	560	565	570	575

■ Confirmed
▨ Probable
□ Possible

Summer resident
Earliest confirmation June 19 – Carrying food
Latest confirmation August 3 – Carrying food

From wintering grounds in western Mexico, Lazuli Bunting arrives in Napa County the last week of April. Migrants are widespread and sometimes abundant, especially in the hills east of the Napa Valley. Those that settle to nest prefer broken chaparral slopes. They colonize successional, post-wildfire habitat (Greene *et al.* 1996); however, such behavior is undocumented in Napa's hills. Post-breeding dispersal frequently brings buntings into lowland riparian areas during July and August.

Lazuli Bunting was confirmed in three priority blocks during 1993: adults were observed carrying food at upper Putah Creek June 19 and on the slopes above Chiles Valley August 3; fledglings were seen in the Redwood Canyon area June 23. The 22 additional records span May 1-July 5. The May and June timing of Atlas fieldwork may account for the large percentage of weak breeding evidence. Almost one-half of such records were obtained prior to May 14, when presumed breeding birds could have been migrants. The remote, rugged, and hot chaparral habitat is a challenge to access during July, perhaps the height of the season for the county's buntings.

Prior to the Atlas during the 1980s, four records of territorial birds in Jamieson Canyon span May 15-July 15, and adults were attending young there on June 30, 1987. Farther back, a nest with young was found along Deer Park Road on July 15, 1950. Grinnell and Wythe (1927) considered Lazuli Bunting a common summer resident. Its breeding status and distribution in Napa County are not well understood.

Sponsored by Joanne Castro

RED-WINGED BLACKBIRD
Agelaius phoeniceus

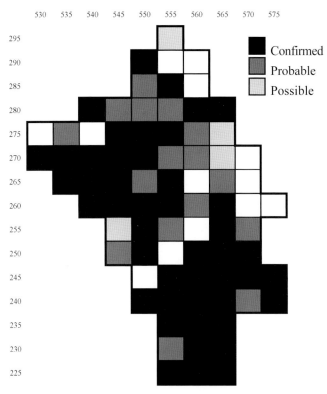

Confirmed
Probable
Possible

Year-round resident
Earliest confirmation March 31 – Carrying nesting material
Latest confirmation July 4 – Carrying food

The Red-winged Blackbird is noisy, brazen, and widespread. Therefore, it is the singularly well-known blackbird of the West. It prefers permanently watered habitats, salt or fresh, including tidal and fresh-water marshes, lakes, ponds, and streams. Breeding red-wingeds frequently form colonies, or a lone pair may claim a patch of isolated cattails growing from a wet depression. They take advantage of any human-created opportunity such as roadside ditches and irrigation ponds.

Atlas data was concentrated during May and June. Yasukawa and Searcy (1995) describe mid-April as the primary nest-building period in central California. Second broods are rare, or rarely successful, and nesting is completed by mid-June. Bent (1958) reported 360 egg dates throughout California, March 26-June 26. Seven Atlas nest construction records span March 31-May 25. Nests with eggs were found May 1 and 5, 1989, at adjacent northern Napa Valley blocks, and nestlings were in four blocks between April 14 at Napa and June 8 near Foss Valley. Adults were carrying food for young in 10 blocks May 1-June 10 and on July 4 at Pope Canyon. Ten fledgling dates span May 2-June 20 and five June 28-July 4. Abundance was estimated to exceed 100 pairs in five blocks: two in Pope Valley, two encompassing the Putah Creek arm of Lake Berryessa, and one south of Napa Valley College.

Red-winged Blackbirds are a presence throughout the county wherever suitable habitat exists. Especially in terms of abundance, blackbirds depend on human-created habitat across much of the interior east of the Napa Valley.

Sponsored by Eleanor Dommerich

TRICOLORED BLACKBIRD
Agelaius tricolor

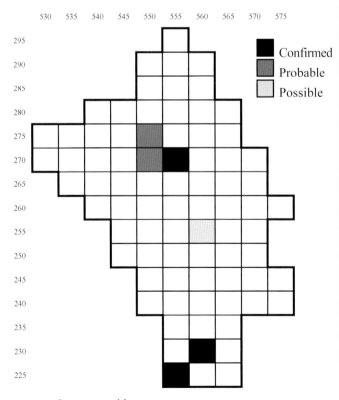

Confirmed
Probable
Possible

Summer resident
Earliest confirmation May 21 – Feeding young
Latest confirmation July 1 – Feeding young

The sound of an early spring flock of Tricolored Blackbirds is memorable in its ear-jangling dissonance. Flocks coalesce to form the largest colonies of any North American bird (Beedy and Hamilton 1999). Napa County colonies are relatively small, rarely exceeding 100 pairs. Traditionally nesting primarily in fresh-water marshes, tricoloreds increasingly nest in overgrown weedy fields and in thickets of Himalayan Blackberry (Jaramillo and Burke 1999). Nesting birds forage in open country away from the colony, frequently where livestock are present (Beedy and Hamilton 1999).

Prior to the Atlas, an April 1986 nest with eggs at a ranch in Pope Valley was the only county breeding record. Three Pope Valley blocks reported Tricolored Blackbirds during the Atlas: fledglings were in eastern Pope Valley on May 21, 1993, and colonies of 11-100 pairs were observed on May 17 and June 18, 1991, in adjacent blocks in central Pope Valley. Fledglings were seen on June 22, 1991, at a similarly sized colony south of the city of Napa. A newly created marsh at Huichica Creek Wildlife Area supported more than 100 pairs on June 13, 1991, when birds were observed building nests as well as feeding fledglings.

The number of colonies in Napa may be limited by a lack of productive foraging areas adjacent to nesting habitat. It is perhaps instructive that our largest colony is located near the small cattle operation at Buchli Station. Because of population declines, Tricolored Blackbird is a Species of Special Concern in California.

WESTERN MEADOWLARK
Sternella neglecta

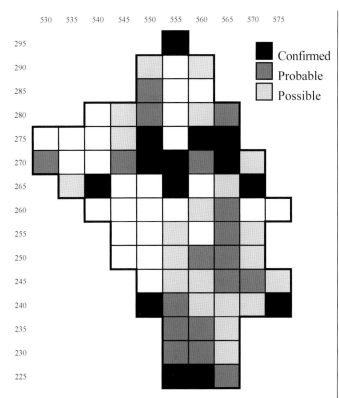

Year-round resident
Earliest confirmation April 18 – Carrying nesting material
Latest confirmation July 18 – Recently fledged young

It doesn't appear to matter to the Western Meadowlark when lush winter grassland is withering to brown, for it is then that its nesting season is beginning. It also has little concern for changes in the composition of its grassland habitat. Meadowlarks have successfully adapted to, or perhaps exploited, the almost complete replacement of perennial native species with exotic annuals. In addition to open grassland, meadowlarks nest at the edges of oak savannah, in both upland and lowland pastures and in hayfields. Pastures and hayfields are increasingly scarce in Napa County.

Mated pairs and territorial males were discovered at a few locations at the end of March; such reports extended primarily from late April into early June. A bird carrying nesting material along Partrick Road on April 18 was the earliest confirmation. A nest with eggs was discovered at Knoxville on June 1. Adults were carrying food for young in seven blocks between May 2 at Lake Berryessa and July 6 near Bothe - the lone Napa Valley confirmation. Fledglings were in Pope Valley on May 14 and through July 18 at Berryessa.

Western Meadowlark is fairly common wherever open grassland remains in the county. The more generous abundance estimates were recorded in Pope, Chiles, and Capell Valleys, the Berryessa shore, and along the Napa River from Kennedy Park south. With a few exceptions, the habitat at these sites continues to be converted to uses unfavorable to secure breeding and wintering populations of Western Meadowlark.

YELLOW-HEADED BLACKBIRD
Xanthocephalus xanthocephalus

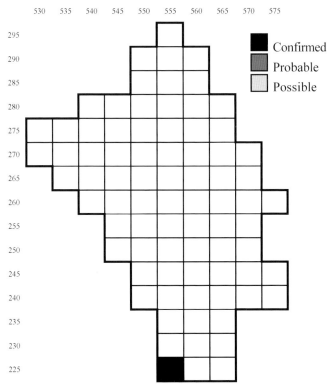

	Confirmed
	Probable
	Possible

Rare summer resident
Only confirmation July 1 – Feeding young

The Yellow-headed Blackbird is a noisy, colonially breeding species of tule and cattail marshes. Nesting birds select the interior portion of a marsh, preferentially "over water of considerable depth," and often forage in adjacent grassland or agricultural fields (Jaramillo and Burke 1999, Grinnell and Miller 1944).

Yellow-headed Blackbirds were found in one priority block. Two pairs were reported at a newly created fresh-water pond at Huichica Creek Wildlife Area on May 18, 1992. The birds were relocated on July 1, when a pair was observed attending a fledgling. In the non-priority block west of American Canyon, Yellow-headed Blackbirds were discovered at fresh-water mitigation ponds on May 24, 1991. Breeding was confirmed by Carl Wilcox and Bruce Walker when they found an estimated five active nests on June 29, 1991. The American Canyon report represents the first breeding record in Napa County.

The Central Valley contains the majority of California's breeding Yellow-headed Blackbirds. In 1972, fewer than 30 colonies were conservatively estimated to support approximately 2000 pairs (Twedt and Crawford 1995). Since the completion of the Atlas, these blackbirds continue to be seen at the fresh-water pond at Huichica Creek Wildlife Area. In 2002 it was proposed that Yellow-headed Blackbird be listed as a Species of Special Concern in California.

BREWER'S BLACKBIRD
Euphagus cyanocephalus

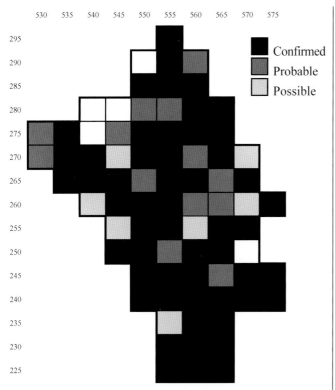

Legend:
- ■ Confirmed
- ▨ Probable
- ☐ Possible

Year-round resident
Earliest confirmation March 26 – Carrying nesting material
Latest confirmation July 8 – Carrying food

That oblivious blackbird foraging on the shoulder of Highway 29 or underfoot at Kennedy Park picnic tables is a Brewer's Blackbird. Grinnell and Miller (1944) understated the situation, writing that it "appears to have increased as a result of human occupancy." Brewer's Blackbirds are common nesting birds along streams, in meadows, at irrigated parks and golf courses, and around ranch buildings. They forage in the open but require thickets of shrubs or belts of trees for nesting and roosting. In the county away from civilization, they breed at isolated springs, watering troughs, and ranch ponds. The account by Williams (1958) in *Bent's Life Histories* gives an exceptionally comprehensive description of the biology of Brewer's Blackbird in California.

Nest construction reports in nine blocks span March 26-June 4. A nest with eggs in the Bothe block April 26 and nestlings at upper Putah Creek June 25 are the only such records. Confirmations were dominated by observations of adults carrying food for young; there are 28 records April 6-July 8, including 18 during May. Fledglings were detected in 10 blocks May 5-June 26. Brewer's Blackbird often breeds colonially; blocks reporting more than 100 pairs include Stanly Ranch and two in Pope Valley. Abundance estimates of 11-100 pairs came from 30 of the 36 reporting blocks.

According to recent Breeding Bird Survey data, the San Francisco Bay Area supports the highest densities of Brewer's Blackbird in the USA (Martin 2002). Absent only in forested or chaparral habitat, it is our most widespread blackbird.

Sponsored by Dick and Carol Eyheralde

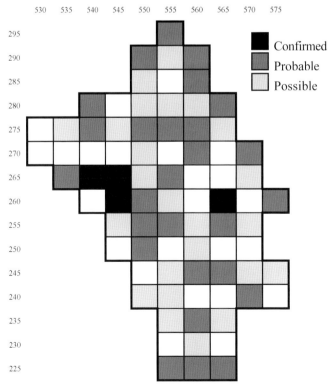

Summer resident
Earliest confirmation May 1 – Recently fledged young
Latest confirmation July 15 – Feeding young

The Brown-headed Cowbird is a brood parasite; a well-nourished female might lay as many as 40 eggs within a territory that she defends through the season (Lowther 1993). Perhaps not present in Napa County before European settlement, cowbirds have "increased phenomenally" in the San Francisco Bay Area since 1922 (Grinnell & Miller 1944). Optimum cowbird habitat is a forest and field ecotone (Lowther 1993), and access to livestock is important as a source of insects and grain.

Cowbirds were confirmed breeding in only four of the 55 priority blocks in which they were found. There were two confirmations in the Napa Valley, one in Angwin, and one at Lake Berryessa. The latter record reported the host species as Orange-crowned Warbler. Eighty percent of the 27 probable records refer to pairs or singing males, primarily between April 27 and June 11. Possible records, the observation of a male or female in proper breeding habitat, span April 16-June 3. Cowbirds were not very common. Estimates of ten pairs or fewer came from 14 of the 19 blocks reporting.

County historical breeding records include fledglings at Aetna Springs in 1972. Fifteen records from the Napa Valley and Alta Heights between 1981 and 1988 record seven host species: Hutton's and Cassin's Vireo, Orange-crowned, Yellow, and Wilson's Warbler, Song Sparrow, and Black-headed Grosbeak; Oak Titmouse has also been reported. Why the Atlas recorded so few confirmations for this uncommon but widespread species is unclear. One hopes it reflects the cowbird's diminishing success.

HOODED ORIOLE
Icterus cucullatus

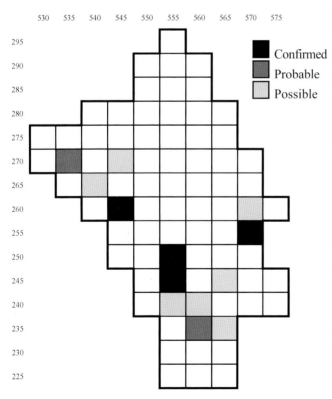

Legend:
- ■ Confirmed
- ▮ Probable
- ▯ Possible

Summer resident
Earliest confirmation May 22 – Recently fledged
young
Latest confirmation June 15 – Nest building

The Hooded Oriole has followed our exotic plantings of palms and shade trees north from its original range in California's southern deserts, reaching the San Francisco Bay Area in 1930 (Grinnell and Miller 1944). Washington and date palms are the favored species in which to construct nests, and abundant, mature shade trees complete its habitat needs in residential and urban districts throughout the Bay Area. Because Hooded Orioles nest high in the trees and sing very briefly upon their arrival in spring (Robin Leong, pers. comm.), they are easily overlooked despite their brilliant coloring.

Hooded Oriole was found in 14 priority blocks. The four confirmations include fledglings at St. Helena on May 22, 1989; an occupied nest on June 3 and nest building on June 15, both around Yountville in 1990; and adults feeding fledglings just south of Lake Berryessa on May 28, 1993. Pairs were observed in Napa and Calistoga in 1993 during April and June, respectively. There is a May 18 record of a possible breeding bird at Angwin. Six of the eight blocks estimating abundance reported a single pair.

Except for the east-central reports, each positive and potential breeding record comes from densely settled areas of the county, primarily the Napa Valley floor. While palms have always been the preferred nest site, recent evidence reveals that Hooded Oriole is also nesting in oaks (R. Leong, pers. comm.). Historically, two of the county's most reliable breeding locations are Fuller Park in Napa and Lewelling Lane in St. Helena.

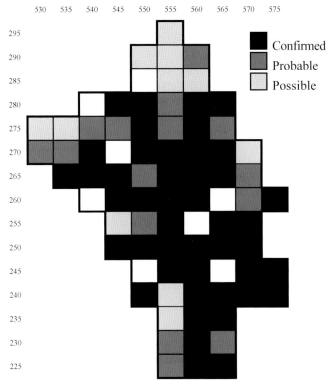

	Confirmed
	Probable
	Possible

Summer resident
Earliest confirmation April 3 – Carrying nesting material
Latest confirmation July 5 – Feeding young

Bullock's Oriole is the familiar oriole throughout most of California and the western United States. Bullock's Orioles are conspicuous during early spring in riparian and oak woodland and are also found in open ranch country with scattered stands of large trees. In most situations they prefer larger, often isolated clumps of trees (Grinnell and Miller 1944). Bullock's Oriole is known to form crèches of up to 100 individuals after fledging (Rising and Williams 1999). Concentrations of 20-30 birds are seen annually during July at the Napa River Ecological Reserve.

Orioles appear in Napa by the end of March. Atlas data records nest construction in ten blocks between April 9 - May 4 and at Coombsville on June 2. A May 2 nest with young at northwestern Lake Berryessa precedes five additional records spanning May 21-June 12. Fledglings were detected in 16 blocks between May 24 at Capell Valley and July 7 at Trout Creek Ridge. The majority of probable data refers to pairs present during May and June. Earlier records include a mated pair southeast of Angwin on March 28 and courtship behavior noted at southeastern Berryessa on April 5.

Bullock's Oriole is common over most of the county. Chaparral and conifer habitats around Knoxville and Mt. St. Helena support fewer birds. Since riparian woodland is important habitat for both nesting and post-breeding dispersal, Bullock's Oriole is a splendid example to show that it is not only rare and unusual species which depend upon vital riparian corridors.

PURPLE FINCH
Carpodacus purpureus

EDWARD ROOKS © 2001

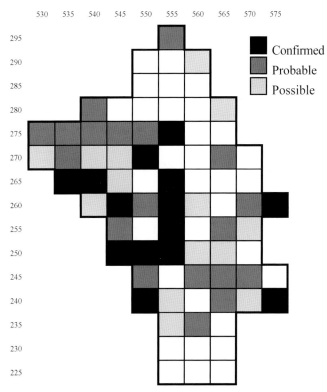

Confirmed
Probable
Possible

Year-round resident
Earliest confirmation April 16 – Carrying nesting
material
Latest confirmation June 16 – Feeding young

During the month of April, a Purple Finch singing from the tip of a Douglas fir represents the essence of the mixed forests and canyons of the western hills. Fewer birds inhabit upland areas where conifers are lacking, and so their presence is scattered. Napa Valley riparian corridors support a small share of the county's breeding population. Purple Finch is often common at the edges of urban areas during the winter, sometimes at feeders. For nesting, however, it distinctly prefers native plant communities.

Purple Finch was discovered building nests between April 16 at St. Helena and June 3 near Yountville. A nest with young was found northeast of Pope Valley on May 31. Fledglings were seen May 1 near Oakville and at seven additional locations May 21-June 16. Probable data of pairs and territorial singing males is distributed throughout May and June. Abundance was estimated in 40 percent of reporting priority blocks. The number of pairs per block was clearly judged greatest in the western hills and the Mt. St. Helena area.

The Atlas revealed Purple Finch to be fairly common in mixed coniferous forests in areas such as Redwood Canyon, Bothe, and Los Posadas. It is locally distributed in canyon habitat northeast of the city of Napa. Historical breeding records show that Purple Finch is also successful in quality riparian woodland habitat such as the Napa River Ecological Reserve.

HOUSE FINCH
Carpodacus mexicanus

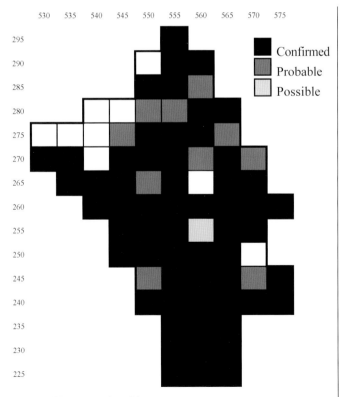

Year-round resident
Earliest confirmation March 15 – Carrying nesting material
Latest confirmation July 11 – Feeding young

Confirmed
Probable
Possible

Perhaps only the European Starling and the House Sparrow rival the House Finch in its ability to take advantage of the bounty found around human settlement. It is also a native species, doing well in native habitats such as chaparral and riparian woodland. As a result, it is one of our most abundant resident birds. Garden nesting birds frequently choose an artificial nest site beneath the eaves or in a basket of flowers. House Finches commonly raise two broods (Woods 1968), and the presence of drinking water is important during the breeding season (Hill 1993). The effects of drought on distribution and nest timing during the Atlas were probably slight.

Nest construction in 24 blocks begins at Pope Valley March 25 and extends through June 23 at Carneros; 17 such records span April 3-May 4. Nestlings were seen in four blocks between May 1 near Angwin and May 15 at Knoxville. Twenty-one fledgling dates span May 1-July 22 and include 13 after May 30. Egg dates are lacking. Just prior to the Atlas period, four egg dates at Fly Bay span May 30-June 28, 1988. The large number of confirmations during April and May reflects the California season reported by Woods (1968).

House Finches were markedly absent from the high elevation and relatively densely forested blocks at the northwestern border of the county. This probably reflects a true absence due to lack of breeding habitat, including water, rather than the difficulties of accessing parts of this more remote region.

PINE SISKIN
Carduelis pinus

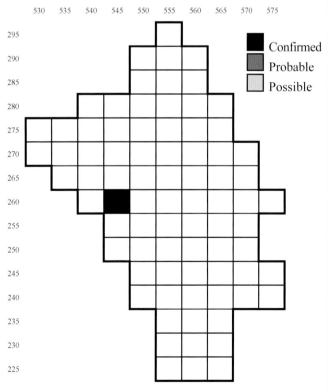

Rare summer visitor, winter resident
Only confirmation June 8 – Recently fledged young

Pine Siskin numbers are variable within and between winters in Napa County. Flocks exploit an available food resource either as long as it lasts or until their vagabond nature puts them to flight. On the northern California coast, it is a common breeding species in open, native coniferous forest; fewer birds use planted conifers and eucalyptus (Palmer 1968, Shuford 1993). Pine Siskin is very rare in Napa County after April, and, until 1991, there were no breeding records.

In late April 1991, two possibly different siskins were reported carrying nesting material in two backyards near the Pope Street bridge in St. Helena. An empty nest in a Colorado blue spruce was described there on May 15, and an adult accompanied a fledgling to a thistle feeder on June 8. Up to 100 siskins had frequented the yard through March 31, with fewer than ten remaining into May. In Michigan (Hull 1989) and Wisconsin, unusual breeding records in the vicinity of feeders are known to occur following winters when siskins were particularly abundant. Elsewhere during the Atlas, Pine Siskin was observed at Mt. St. Helena on May 25, 1992, and at two locations on May 1, 1993.

Pine Siskin is a winter visitor to Napa County. It should be looked for as a possible breeding species during any year following a large winter presence. Ornamental conifers may offer the only suitable breeding habitat in the county.

LESSER GOLDFINCH
Carduelis psaltria

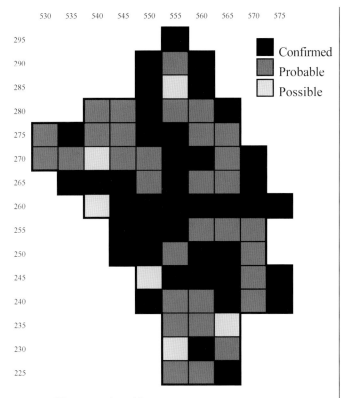

Year-round resident
Earliest confirmation April 9 – Carrying nesting material
Latest confirmation July 18 – Recently fledged young

The Lesser Goldfinch may be found almost everywhere, on nearly any day, yet each encounter is unique and something of a surprise. It wanders much of the year, lingering wherever a food plant has set seed, and is common in oak savannah and riparian woodland, open chaparral, fields, towns, and gardens. It requires a source of fresh water (Watt and Willoughby 1999). Lesser Goldfinch is the only species to be found in all 79 Atlas priority blocks.

At Carmel Valley's Hastings Reservation, nesting regularly begins mid-April, peaking during May; egg dates throughout the state range from April 2-August 3 (Linsdale 1968, Watt and Willoughby 1999). The seven Atlas nest construction reports span April 9-June 20; five are April records. Nests with eggs were found at Wragg Ridge May 13 and Jamieson Canyon May 26. Nestlings were discovered in five blocks May 26-June 6. One-half of the 24 records of fledglings were during June; there were four May records and eight during July through the 18th southwest of Lake Hennessey. Probable records primarily describe mated pairs between late March and late July. Abundance estimates exceeded 11 pairs in 38 of the 46 reporting blocks.

Lesser Goldfinch has adapted to the human presence, taking advantage of both native and exotic seasonal foraging opportunities. Yellow star thistle, the introduced scourge of grassland and savannah, is a favorite of winter flocks. Linsdale (1968) describes fiddleneck and chamise as important summer foods.

LAWRENCE'S GOLDFINCH
Carduelis lawrencei

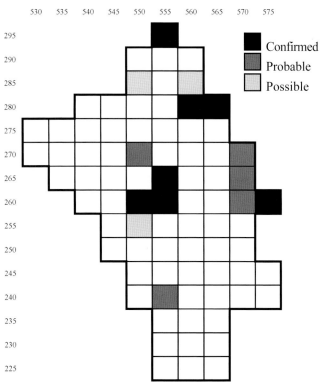

Confirmed
Probable
Possible

Summer resident, occasional winter visitor
Earliest confirmation April 20 – Nest building
Latest confirmation July 16 – Recently fledged young

Lawrence's Goldfinch is known for its erratic, unreliable breeding distribution. However, there are a couple of places in Napa County where it is found nearly every summer: the hot, open, blue oak margins of Lake Hennessey and Lake Berryessa. The main population is well to the south of Napa; e.g., 2000-5000 pairs were estimated in Monterey Co. during the 1980s (Davis 1999). Lawrence's Goldfinch favors open oak woodland and adjacent chaparral or grassland where chamise and annual herbs provide food at varying periods of the year (Grinnell and Miller 1944). Breeding sites require a source of water within 0.30 miles (Davis 1999).

Lawrence's Goldfinch was found at nine blocks touching on the traditional Hennessey and Berryessa sites. Berryessa confirmations include nest building April 20, an occupied nest April 27, and adults feeding fledglings June 1. Mated pairs were found in three additional Berryessa blocks during May. Birds at Hennessey were carrying nesting material on June 2 and fledglings were seen July 16. Fledglings were found July 2 in nearby Chiles Valley as well. Atlasers discovered mated pairs at Pope Valley and northwest Napa city.

Napa County is located at the northern and western fringes of the summer range of Lawrence's Goldfinch. The breeding population probably does not exceed 50 pairs in any given year, but this goldfinch was found during each of the five Atlas seasons. There are a few winter records from Berryessa, Hennessey, and Napa River Ecological Reserve.

Sponsored by Bruce and Marjorie Irwin

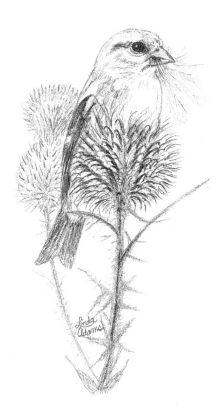

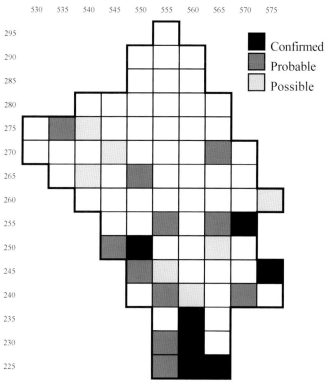

Confirmed
Probable
Possible

Year-round resident, more widespread in winter
Earliest confirmation April 9 – Carrying nesting material
Latest confirmation July 15 – Recently fledged young

The male American Goldfinch marks the beginnings of its breeding season by transforming itself from a dim brown and green bird into one of brilliant yellow and black. It is restricted to open country with sufficient small trees, often willow, or shrubs in which to place its nest. Overgrown fields and roadsides provide it with the compositae species, such as thistle and chicory, which are its primary food source through the year (Middleton 1993). Such weedy fields are increasingly scarce in Napa County. The scattered fall and winter flocks are small, and it is an uncommon nesting bird.

The breeding season in the county is relatively late for this goldfinch; five of seven confirmations span June 10-July 15 and include fledglings in three blocks after July 8. Goldfinches were carrying nesting material on April 9 at Lake Curry; during early spring such behavior is not always indicative of nesting. Ninety percent of probable records refer to mated pairs, primarily during late April and early May.

The southern marsh and pasture country supports the majority of our nesting American Goldfinches. Breeding bird densities are low in the Napa Valley and interior valleys. The high humidity associated with summer fog presumably provides a more abundant seed crop in the south (Shuford 1993), and nestlings are raised almost entirely on seeds. The brushy levees at Huichica Creek Wildlife Area are a convenient area to see nesting goldfinches.

HOUSE SPARROW
Passer domesticus

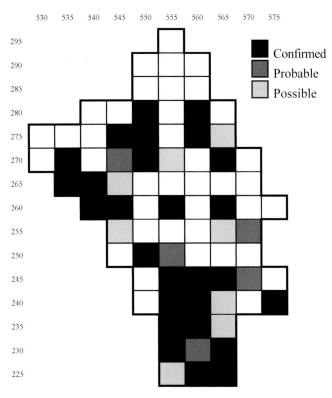

530 535 540 545 550 555 560 565 570 575

295
290
285
280
275
270
265
260
255
250
245
240
235
230
225

■ Confirmed
▨ Probable
▢ Possible

Year-round resident
Earliest confirmation April 3 –Nest building
Latest confirmation August 4 – Feeding young

About ranches and towns throughout the county, the voice of the House Sparrow may often be the first living sound to drift into human consciousness each morning. Seeking the debris of agriculture and burger joints for food, and the shelter of buildings and bridges for nesting, House Sparrows find us agreeable companions. It is unfortunate that, although supremely clever and industrious, they cannot exist in America without us.

House Sparrows were confirmed in 27 priority blocks. Birds were building nests in six blocks April 3-May 2 and in Jamieson Canyon on June 16. Eggs were in a nest at northern Lake Berryessa May 1 and nestlings at Aetna Springs May 12. Adults carrying food for young were at seven locations May 13-June 26, and nine fledgling reports were scattered between April 15 and August 4. Atlasers estimated abundance levels of 101-1000 pairs in four different blocks the length of the Napa Valley. The nine blocks supporting 11-100 pairs included three additional valley blocks, all four touching Pope Valley, and two on the Berryessa shore.

As is the case with native species, the range of the exotic House Sparrow closely follows available habitat. Each block on the map surely contains human settlement or at least a shed and a couple of horses. The conversion of the county to viticulture, plus a reduced livestock industry, has probably decreased the population over the past half-century. However, this adaptable bird will never be far from the edge of town or the back of a barn.

OTHER BIRDS

Former

There is one historical nesting record for the California Condor – an egg taken August 16, 1845, which now resides in a Russian Museum. Yellow-billed Cuckoo was confirmed (occupied nest) on June 15, 1902, by E.L. Bickford on Soda Springs Road by the "Wilson Ranch." Mr. Bickford also found Bank Swallow on an occupied nest on June 15, 1930, near Hwy. 121 and Trancas St., Napa. Black-chinned Sparrow was confirmed July 9, 1984, by Murray Berner, when he found an adult feeding a fledgling at the southeastern Palisades. These species were not observed during the Atlas period. The California Condor's plight (extirpated in Napa County) has been well documented, and suitable habitat for Yellow-billed Cuckoo and Bank Swallow probably no longer exists. The Caspian Tern and Cedar Waxwing formerly bred in Napa County, but Napa atlasers only observed these two species and were unable to obtain objective evidence of breeding.

Caspian Tern (*Sterna caspia*)

Caspian Tern is common over Napa County waters during summer. It nested at Little Island in 1977 (Gill 1977) and at Island No. 2 in 1987. The latter site was lost when levee reinforcement work covered the sand substrate used by the terns. In 1989 two breeding colonies were discovered at Knight Island in Solano County (Bailey *et al.* 1989), within three miles of the historical Island No. 2 colony. Those colonies remain active. As tidal marsh is altered naturally or by restoration efforts, a breeding site may once again develop in Napa County. Non-breeding terns were observed in 23 Atlas blocks between April 15-July 18.

Cedar Waxwing (*Bombycilla cedrorum*)

Historically, Cedar Waxwing occupied a nest at Linda Falls, Conn Creek, June 15, 1973; it is the lone North Bay breeding record (William G. Bousman, unpubl. data). Typically, the large winter flocks dwindle by mid-March. Migrant flocks reappear during late April and are encountered through about May 20. Exceptionally, a few linger into June. The pair bond is often established by April, and courtship behavior within migrant flocks is documented in California (Whitmer *et al.* 1997, Feltes 1936). Migrants were observed during the Atlas as late as June 3. The normal breeding range in California is confined to the northwest coast.

Potential (Species that have never been confirmed breeding in Napa County)

Special Note: Of the probable and possible breeders found during the Atlas period, Blue-winged Teal, Short-eared Owl, Black-chinned Hummingbird, Dusky Flycatcher, and Phainopepla have never been confirmed breeding in Napa County.

American Bittern (*Botaurus lentiginosus*)

The American Bittern is secretive and infrequently seen. Small numbers winter in the Napa Marsh. In western North America it apparently nests only in fresh-water marsh (Shuford 1993). In Solano County, it breeds in Suisun Marsh, and the Sonoma Atlas reported bitterns at six locations, including one tidal marsh block (Burridge 1995). The Napa Atlas recorded a single bird near Buchli Station on April 2, 1990. American Bittern has never been seen outside of our tidal district, where fresh-water marsh is essentially nonexistent. Bitterns attempting to nest in Napa County may have no alternative to brackish conditions.

Mandarin Duck (*Aix galericulata*)

Mandarin Duck is the East Asian counterpart to our native Wood Duck. Several hundred introduced birds exist in a free-flying state within ten miles of Calistoga at Indian Meadow Ranch, Sonoma County (Shurtleff and Savage 1996). With its origins at that ranch, a feral population has developed in the Calistoga area. The Atlas recorded a mated pair at the wastewater treatment facility May 15, 1990, and a female with young at Blossom Creek July 12, 1993. Mandarins continue to be seen around Calistoga. As a potential competitive threat to native Wood Ducks, the Mandarin should probably be discouraged from becoming established in California. The American Ornithologists' Union does not yet recognize this duck as self-sustaining in the wild.

Canvasback (*Aythya valisineria*)

A female Canvasback seen at the Soscol Ferry Road water treatment facility on July 27, 1990, represents the lone Atlas report. Away from the Great Basin, it is an irregularly breeding bird in the Central Valley and accidental in the Bay Area (Mowbray 2002, William G. Bousman, unpubl. data), including two Solano County nesting records (Conrad Jones, pers. comm.). Canvasback has yet to breed in Napa. The county's bay and river district is regarded primarily as vitally important wintering habitat.

Wilson's Phalarope (*Phalaropus tricolor*)

Wilson's Phalarope was seen in two tidal blocks: a flock of 20 birds June 1, 1991, and a pair June 7, 1993. The birds were not seen again and were presumed to be migrants. In California, phalaropes nest primarily in Great Basin short grass or sedge marsh. Similar habitat existed at Huichica Creek Wildlife Area in 1986; Wilson's Phalaropes were present throughout June, and a juvenile-plumaged bird (apparently flightless) was seen on July 1. A Sonoma atlas confirmation was obtained that year 13 miles west of Huichica (Burridge 1995). At present, nesting habitat is lacking in Napa County and breeding is unlikely.

Western Gull *(Larus occidentalis)*

Western Gull was observed in several tidal district blocks, primarily at the Solano County line. Gulls currently nest on derelict pilings in the Napa River at Mare Island, four miles from Napa County, where there are no breeding records. Similar sites along the river in Napa include the Can Club duck blinds, an ancient shipwreck at Slaughterhouse Point, Napa River channel marker buoys, and the usually idle railroad bridge near Green Island Road.

Uncertain

Lesser Scaup *(Aythya affinis)*

Two tidal district blocks reported Lesser Scaup in 1992: a possibly mated pair and three males June 13, and a second pair on June 27. Also in 1992 during the Santa Clara County atlas, nine broods were seen at the Sunnyvale water treatment facility, the first breeding records in California away from the Great Basin (Bailey *et al.* 1992). The continental population, including Tule Lake Basin in California, nests in fresh to moderately brackish seasonal or semi-permanent wetlands (Austin *et al.* 1998). The north San Francisco Bay region remains without a breeding record (William G. Bousman, unpubl. data).

Rare Breeders

The following species had just one confirmed nesting record for the Atlas period: Great Egret, Mandarin Duck, Northern Shoveler, Bald Eagle, Ring-necked Pheasant, Greater Roadrunner, Long-eared Owl, American Dipper, Swainson's Thrush, Hermit Thrush, Yellow-breasted Chat, and Pine Siskin.

New Breeding Species

The Atlas confirmed the following species breeding for the first time in Napa County: Clark's Grebe, Great Egret, Snowy Egret, Bald Eagle, Spotted Sandpiper, Forster's Tern, Greater Roadrunner, Long-eared Owl, Yellow-billed Magpie, Red-breasted Nuthatch, Grasshopper Sparrow, Yellow-headed Blackbird, and Pine Siskin, plus Mandarin Duck.

Breeding Status Irregular or Unclear

Species with either irregular and/or unclear breeding status in Napa County include Clark's and Western Grebe, Long-eared Owl, Northern Saw-whet Owl, Dusky Flycatcher, Red-breasted Nuthatch, Hermit Warbler (found breeding after the Atlas period), Yellow-rumped Warbler, Pine Siskin, and Lawrence's Goldfinch.

Napa County Breeding Birds
Threatened, Endangered, California Species of Concern

Double-crested Cormorant	(CSC)
Osprey	(CSC)
Bald Eagle	FT
Northern Harrier	CSC, 2
Cooper's Hawk	(CSC)
Sharp-shinned Hawk	(CSC)
Golden Eagle	(CSC)
Prairie Falcon	CSC, 3
California Black Rail	ST
California Clapper Rail	SE, FE
Western Snowy Plover—(coastal)	(CSC) FT
Burrowing Owl	CSC, 1
Long-eared Owl	CSC, 2
Short-eared Owl	CSC, 2
Northern Spotted Owl	FT
Olive-sided Flycatcher	CSC, 2
Loggerhead Shrike	CSC, 2
California Horned Lark	CSC, 3
Purple Martin	CSC, 1
California Swainson's Thrush	CSC, 3
Yellow Warbler	CSC, 2
San Francisco Common Yellowthroat	CSC, 1
Yellow-breasted Chat	CSC, 3
Bell's Sage Sparrow	CSC, 1
Grasshopper Sparrow	[CSC], 2
San Pablo or Samuel's Song Sparrow	CSC, 2
Tricolored Blackbird	CSC, 2
Yellow-headed Blackbird	[CSC], 2

Codes

CSC ~ California Species of Concern - on current and draft revised lists

(CSC)~ California Species of Concern - on current list, but not on draft revised list

[CSC]~ California Species of Concern - not on current list, but on draft revised list

1,2,3 ~ Category of CSC for State listing as Threatened or Endangered

ST ~ State Threatened

SE ~ State Endangered

FT ~ Federal Threatened

FE ~ Federal Endangered

(Federal list dated September 24, 2002, Draft Calif. Dept. of Fish and Game August 1, 2002)

BIOGEOGRAPHY

Napa County is favored with a diverse breeding avifauna. It is a relatively small California county at approximately 780 square miles (ranked 49th in size of 58 counties), but its geographic location ensures a complex ecosystem. Located at the margins of three major biological regions (the northern reaches of the San Francisco Bay-Delta estuary, the western edge of the Sacramento Valley, and divided north-to-south by several extensions of the Coast Range), Napa County exhibits a high level of biological diversity. That diversity is documented by the 156 species of breeding birds found within the county's borders over the five-year span of the Breeding Bird Atlas survey.

Along with the ecotone influence on species abundance, the county is also topographically varied. Elevations range from sea level in the south at San Pablo Bay to nearly 4,300' on the higher peaks and ridges in the northwest section of the county near Mount St. Helena. Major topographic features include three usually well-defined northwest/southeast-oriented mountain ranges and the expansive, mostly tidal, Napa Marsh, together with the river and creek valleys associated with the mountain ranges and the marsh.

The county's western boundary with Sonoma County is marked by the ridgelines of the Mayacamas and Sonoma mountains. The world-renowned fertile grape-growing Napa Valley is bordered by these mountains on its western flank and primarily by the Howell Mountains on its eastern flank. The floor of the Valley extends from the northwest corner of the county at the base of Mount St. Helena to the northern reach of the Napa River estuary at the city of Napa. The fifty-mile-long Napa River and its nearly 50 tributaries drain the Napa Valley watershed. The Valley is also the center of the county's population, from the cities of Calistoga and St. Helena in the north, to Yountville and the county seat of Napa in the south. The county's fifth incorporated municipality, American Canyon, is located along the estuarine extension of the Napa River at Napa County's southern boundary with Solano County. There are smaller unincorporated urban enclaves in Angwin, Deer Park, Coombsville, Pope Valley, Wooden Valley and Lake Berryessa that contribute to an overall county population of 125,000 at the 2000 census.

The Palisades extension of Mount St. Helena, the Howell Mountains, Cedar Roughs, and the Napa ranges associated with Atlas Peak separate the Napa Valley from the eastern county Pope, Wooden and Berryessa Valleys. These three watersheds are drained primarily by Pope, Wooden Valley and Putah Creeks, which flow southeasterly and ultimately discharge into the Sacramento River/Delta. The largest of these valleys, Berryessa, is almost entirely inundated by the impounded waters of the largest fresh-water topographic feature of the county, Lake Berryessa. The easternmost mountains of the Putah Creek watershed also delineate the county's east boundary. This border is clearly demarcated by the distinctive north Blue Ridge, Rocky Ridge, south Blue Ridge, and Vaca Mountains from north to south respectively.

Napa County's weather can generally be described as a mild Mediterranean climate. Rainfall is sharply seasonal from November through April, while the May through October months are an essentially precipitation-free period. Rainfall is greatly influenced locally by the north/south-oriented alternating ridgelines and valleys as well as the north/south descending elevation gradient. Annual rainfall averages approach 50-60 inches at the higher elevations in the Mayacamas-Sonoma mountains in west Napa County and fall off to about 20-25 inches in the east from the rain shadow effect of the intervening ridgelines. The decreasing elevation gradient from north to south is also reflected in precipitation patterns. The lowest rainfall totals in the county are near sea level in southern Napa County, where annual averages are on the order of 18-20 inches.

Countywide temperature averages can be represented by looking at a higher elevation northern site (Angwin, at 1,800' on Howell Mountain) and the lower elevation site of the city of Napa near sea level in south Napa County. The average winter temperature in Angwin is 45°F. and in Napa it is 49°F. Their respective summer averages are 69°F. and 66°F. Summer temperatures in the city of Napa are moderated by the cooler air of nearby San Francisco Bay. On rare occasions the county has experienced extreme lows of 9°F. and highs of 115°F.

Not surprisingly, vegetative cover, variety and complexity (see Vegetation Map) also generally correlate with areas in the county that experience higher precipitation and fewer temperature extremes. The county's higher, wetter areas are dominated by stands of mixed conifer forest comprised mostly of second- and third-growth Douglas fir and coast redwood. Of the county's approximately 495,000 acres of land surface, about 15,000 acres are of this habitat. Breeding birds typical of this area are Steller's Jay, Band-tailed Pigeon, the federally listed Northern Spotted Owl, Western Tanager, Olive-sided Flycatcher, and Purple Finch. Integrating with mixed coniferous forest are approximately 50,000 acres of transitional mixed coniferous/mixed hardwood forest. In addition to the conifers, representative canopy tree species include madrone, California laurel, tan oak, and several other species of oak. Birds breeding in these forests include Pileated Woodpecker, Pacific-slope Flycatcher, Warbling Vireo, and Wilson's Warbler.

The dominant extensive vegetative types clothing the county, however, are those associated with the broader dryer areas on the south slopes of the ranges and in the rain-shadowed eastern mountains. Almost 335,000 acres are covered to a greater or lesser extent by broad-leafed woodlands, broadleaf/pine woodlands, or chaparral. Oak woodland (broadly defined) and oak savannah comprise about 160,000 acres and chaparral about 175,000 acres. Broadleaf woodland/forest can include areas of relatively dense associations of live oak, California laurel, and big-leaf maple, for example, but also areas of rather low-density combinations of deciduous oak, California buckeye, foothill pine, and madrone. The oak woodlands also encompass the increasingly less common valley oak/savannah assemblages. A wide range of birds nest in these diverse, moderately wet to dry woodlands. Some examples are the Red-tailed Hawk, California Quail, Western Screech-Owl, Acorn Woodpecker, Nuttall's Woodpecker, Western Scrub-Jay, Oak

BIOGEOGRAPHY

Titmouse, White-breasted Nuthatch, Western Bluebird, California and Spotted Towhee, and Black-headed Grosbeak.

Common plants of the chaparral and chaparral/mixed hardwood habitats of Napa County include chamise, manzanita, various species of Ceanothus, and small, drought-limited species of oak. Moderate patches of chaparral are found throughout county areas of thin soil, south or southwest exposure, and high summer temperatures. The most extensive areas of chaparral, however, are found in the eastern mountains, where winter rainfall is low to moderate and summer temperatures are persistently high (many days higher than 100°F.) Breeding species of birds typically found in these dry, hot, and exposed habitats include Western Scrub-Jay, Wrentit, House Wren, Bewick's Wren, Rock Wren, Blue-gray Gnatcatcher, California Thrasher, California and Spotted Towhee, Sage Sparrow, and Lazuli Bunting.

Grassland habitat has been greatly reduced by cultivation and urbanization. Today, fewer than 10,000 acres remain, mostly in fragmented patches. Some areas of native perennial grasslands persist in the foothills around Napa and Berryessa Valleys. Some relatively large areas of mostly non-native annual grasslands remain in southern Napa County in the Carneros, Jamieson Canyon, and American Canyon vicinities. Some recorded breeding species in these grassland habitats are Loggerhead Shrike, Grasshopper Sparrow, Savannah Sparrow, Western Meadowlark, and Red-winged Blackbird. Birds nesting in nearby woodlands and foraging in the grassland areas include Red-tailed Hawk, American Kestrel, Golden Eagle, Western Bluebird, Western Kingbird, and Mourning Dove.

The Napa Marsh, at the estuarine confluence of the Napa River and San Pablo Bay, is a complex of historic brackish tidal marsh; diked, seasonally wet former marshlands; diked former commercial salt evaporation ponds; and low-lying surrounding grasslands or cultivated vineyards. This approximately 20,000-acre marsh habitat supports a large host of aquatic and marsh-inhabiting birds, including many rare or endangered species. The list of birds found in or adjacent to the Napa Marsh grows on an almost annual basis since the area has become public land, more accessible to birders and scientists. The years of Atlas fieldwork documented new breeding birds for the county as well as identifying new areas of breeding for better known or common species. The list below includes representative species of some of the more prominent bird groups. Water birds include Pied-billed Grebe, Double-crested Cormorant, Black-crowned Night-Heron, Great Blue Heron, Great Egret, Canada Goose (increasing dramatically), Mallard, Cinnamon Teal, Gadwall, Northern Pintail, and Ruddy Duck. Raptors include White-tailed Kite, Northern Harrier, Red-tailed Hawk, and American Kestrel. Ring-necked Pheasant was recorded breeding only in the Napa Marsh. The endangered Clapper Rail and the rare Black Rail breed along the tidal sloughs in emergent intertidal bulrushes, cord grass, cattails, and pickle weed. Of the shorebirds, the rare Snowy Plover nests on dredged sediment islands in the salt ponds, as do Killdeer, American Avocet, and Black-necked Stilt. Forster's Tern nests in small groups on the dredge spoil islands as well. Caspian Tern was also suspected to be

nesting but was not confirmed. Breeding songbirds include Tree Swallow, Cliff Swallow and Barn Swallow, plus Marsh Wren, Horned Lark, Common Yellowthroat, Savannah Sparrow, Song Sparrow, Western Meadowlark, Red-winged Blackbird, Tricolored Blackbird, and Yellow-headed Blackbird. The marsh is changing rapidly with more recent intensive wildlife management and large-scale restoration efforts. It is expected that breeding birds will increase in variety and abundance as the marsh returns to its more vibrant historic state.

Fresh-water habitats in the county are confined almost entirely to human-made ponds and reservoirs. There are no naturally occurring fresh-water lakes in Napa County. Agricultural and municipal impoundments are dispersed throughout the county, providing nesting habitat for waterfowl like Mallard and Canada Goose, for water birds like Common Moorhen and American Coot, and for songbirds such as Song Sparrow. The 25,000-acre Lake Berryessa, confined by Monticello Dam, creates the largest fresh-water environment in Napa County. The waters of Putah and Pope Creeks, held behind the dam since 1957, provide aquatic and shoreline habitat for numerous water birds and water-associated species. In the Atlas survey years, Bald Eagle was first recorded breeding at Lake Berryessa and has subsequently been confirmed breeding at several locations there. Osprey was also confirmed breeding at the lake during the Atlas survey. Canada Goose is abundant at the lake, as are other common waterfowl such as Mallard and Gadwall. The Atlas fieldwork also found Prairie Falcon nesting only in the mountains adjacent to Lake Berryessa. The surrounding oak woodland/chaparral complex was also the only area in the county where Greater Roadrunner and Yellow-billed Magpie were found breeding.

Urban environments account for about 25,000 acres of the county landscape, limited primarily to the five incorporated municipalities. Most of the urban habitat consists of older plantings of mixed native/exotic vegetation, which, when viewed from the air, appear to be islands of semi-dense, fragmented woodlands among the vineyards. Atlas work in the cities revealed an expected mix of early successional invasive species such as House Finch, House Sparrow and European Starling. Exotic plantings attracted several species, including Northern Mockingbird, Hooded Oriole, and Allen's Hummingbird. Many local native birds have adapted to mature urban habitats. Among the many species found breeding in these human-created habitats are Red-shouldered Hawk, California Quail, Common Barn-Owl, Western Scrub-Jay, Bullock's Oriole, Brewer's Blackbird, Black Phoebe, Cliff Swallow, American Crow, and Oak Titmouse.

The other large human-created habitat in the county is nearly 50,000 acres of cultivated vineyards. The majority, about 30,000 acres, lies in the Napa, Pope, Chiles, and Wooden Valleys. More recently, an additional 20,000 acres have been planted in areas at higher elevations, concentrated mainly in the western mountains. Breeding birds found in or adjacent to the farmland include Red-tailed Hawk, American Kestrel, California Quail, Killdeer, European Starling, and Western Meadowlark. In recent years, some grape growers and wineries have increased ground cover plantings and have actively encouraged birds to nest in the vineyards for pest management. Barn Owl boxes, Red-tailed Hawk perch poles, American Kestrel, Western Bluebird, and Violet-green/Tree Swallow nest boxes have become widespread.

Although only a small percentage of the county's landmass, riparian corridors provide critical breeding habitat for a multitude of birds and other species. Perhaps fewer than 500 acres of prime, intact riparian forest remain from historic times, when estimates place the number of acres at closer to 20,000, primarily in the Napa River and Putah Creek flood plains. Species found breeding and nesting in these rich habitats of oaks, alders, willows, elderberry, cottonwood, and tangles of wild grape include Wood Duck, Red-shouldered Hawk, Great Horned Owl, Belted Kingfisher, Downy Woodpecker, Western Wood-Pewee, Black Phoebe, Tree and Violet-green Swallow, Yellow-breasted Chat, and Lesser Goldfinch, to name but a few. There are currently efforts underway to increase, restore, and enhance riparian zones throughout the county.

Napa is a biologically diverse county. Its great variety of habitat presents challenges to biologists and birders, but many rewards as well. Human alterations have been substantial and continue to impact the land. However, much of Napa County remains productive native habitat. Let us work today to ensure that when the next Breeding Bird Atlas is completed, those future bird atlasers find as rich an avian population as presently exists.

---Mike Rippey

WEATHER DURING THE ATLAS PERIOD

The *St. Helena Star*, the source of St. Helena rain records, has been publishing rainfall measurements since 1907, with rain gauges placed near the downtown area. The official yearly rainfall season is July 1 to June 30. St. Helena's wettest year was 1982-1983, when 69.7 inches of rain fell, and the driest year on record was 1975-1976, with only 12.39. The seasonal average is 33.71. From 1989 to 1993, the years of the Atlas study, the rainfall in St. Helena was, respectively, 23.87, 24.08, 25.29, 27.11, and 49.58 inches, for a seasonal average of 29.99, which shows that the Atlas was conducted during a prolonged drought period. Rainfall in St. Helena totaled 18.85 in 1988 and 18.41 in 1994, establishing the extent of the drought. During the Atlas years, rainfall at Bothe-Napa Valley State Park was 31.04, 27.09, 30.37, 31.17, and 52.89, about 3.5 inches above St. Helena's average. Bothe-Napa has an average seasonal rainfall of 44.16 inches, but between 1989-93 the average was only 34.51. See Appendix C for monthly rainfall and average high and low temperatures during 1989-1993 at Bothe-Napa Valley State Park.

Below are weather, migration, and breeding summaries, 1989-1993, condensed in part from the Middle Pacific Coast regional summary in *American Birds*.

1989 Late winter rains briefly alleviated the drought. Parts of the region reported increases over 1988 in breeding pairs of waterfowl, while other areas continued to be adversely affected by low water levels. Uncommon ducks summered at unusual locations due both to drought and to ongoing human-caused degradation of nesting habitat. Passerine migration extended into early June; regional reports of late migrants included a variety of flycatchers, Warbling Vireo, Swainson's Thrush, Yellow and Wilson's Warbler, and Black-headed Grosbeak (Erickson *et al.* 1989, Bailey *et al.* 1989).

1990 Drought continued to affect California's waterfowl. Rainfall during May helped create additional brood water, but reproduction was reduced from 1989 (Yee *et al.* 1990). The late May rain also decimated many young birds that were ready to fledge, reducing the success of the breeding season. As the state's drought turned into one of the worst of the century, it appeared to have adverse effects on nesting land birds, such as Barn Owl. The county experienced record low temperatures in later December. The length and severity of the "Big Freeze" resulted in widespread vegetation and insect mortality, affecting primarily hummingbirds and insectivores, residents and winter visitors alike (Yee *et al.* 1990). Atlas fieldwork during the following spring documented the short-term decline of several species. Many raptor nests were revealed when exotic vegetation such as eucalyptus died or lost their leaves.

1991 Heavy March rains supplied temporary relief to drought-impacted wetlands, increasing breeding success of waterfowl and "aquatic" songbirds such as Tricolored Blackbird. Around the region, reports indicated a later-than-normal departure of wintering birds, while spring migrants arrived about two weeks late. Migration was considered outstanding (Yee *et al.* 1991). The continued drought may have encouraged growth of the aquatic vegetation used in Western and Clark's Grebe nests.

1992 Signs of an El Niño event continued during spring and summer. The drought persisted; in apparent response, increased numbers of dabbling ducks nested at regional water treatment facilities. Migration was early, with numerous early arrival dates, but involved relatively small concentrations of birds. It was suggested that lush spring vegetation south of the region served to disperse migrants across a broad front (Bailey *et al.* 1992, Yee *et al.* 1992).

1993 The rainy season continued into spring, ending the "Atlas" drought. A variety of species re-established themselves in habitat made unsuitable during the dry years. The regional land bird migration began in March and was considered notably early; migration subsided during April, gaining momentum during the second week of May when sparrows and buntings were well represented (Yee *et al.* 1993).

EXPLANATION OF A BREEDING BIRD ATLAS

Bird enthusiasts enjoy feeding birds, identifying them, keeping lists, and observing behavior. In winter one may wonder whether the birds present will remain to breed, and in spring whether birds are nesting locally or simply migrants passing through. Birding guides give a general idea of where birds are distributed nationally, and bird lists at parks or reserves provide information about nesting birds in those specific locations. A breeding bird atlas provides, in a readable, easy-to-use format, all the pieces of the puzzle for one particular county.

Breeding Birds of Napa County, California has a series of maps of the county divided into small blocks, each map demonstrating where a particular species was found breeding in Napa between 1989 and 1993. Patterns of darkened squares on the map show the breeding range for that species. Accompanying the map is a narrative describing the bird's breeding habitat, density, and timing, unique to Napa County, with an original artist's rendition of the species, often depicting a characteristic breeding behavior.

Primarily during the first half of the 20th century, Grinnell and Miller and their graduate students documented the distribution of California's birds. Their volume included species maps depicting the counties, while the text described a wealth of specific breeding records. Previous studies of birds in Napa were specific only to habitat, area, or species. *Breeding Birds of Napa County* is the first systematic breeding survey of the county.

The first breeding bird atlas was begun in Great Britain and Ireland in 1966, inspired by a similar atlas of British flora done in the 1950s. It was followed by *The Atlas of Breeding Birds of Britain and Ireland,* for which 10,000 birders did fieldwork from 1968-1972. Since then, interest in atlasing has grown worldwide. Much of Europe has been atlased, and atlas projects have been completed in many states and Canadian provinces (Shuford 1993).

In California, because of its vast size and clustering of birdwatchers in groups such as Audubon chapters, atlasing was initiated at the county level. Bob Stewart, then a biologist at the Point Reyes Bird Observatory, started California's first breeding bird atlas in Marin County in 1976 (Shuford 1993). Fieldwork was completed in 1982 and the atlas published in 1993. Completed atlas projects include Alameda, Contra Costa, Los Angeles, Monterey (published 1993), Orange (published in 1997), Sacramento, San Diego, San Francisco, San Luis Obispo, San Mateo (published 2001), Santa Clara, Santa Cruz, and Sonoma (published 1995). Atlas projects in San Bernadino and Riverside are not yet completed.

The idea for Napa County's breeding bird atlas germinated at a Western Field Ornithology Conference in Monterey in February 1986. Robin Leong, a Napa-Solano Audubon Society (NSAS) member, learned that Marin County had finished a breeding bird atlas, Orange and San Bernardino County atlases were in progress, and Monterey, Sonoma, and Sacramento Counties were considering atlases. The main topics of discussion at the meeting were the correct use of breeding codes, proper study plot sizes, block completion, and priority block choice when there were too many blocks and too few atlasers. Further information was sought at an American Ornithologists' Union (AOU) meeting in San Francisco in August 1987, which included a meeting of the North American Breeding Bird Atlas Conference to discuss breeding bird atlas standards, where valuable contacts were made. Much-needed advice on how to set up a breeding bird atlas was shared by those responsible for publishing them in other counties: Tim Manolis (Sacramento County), Betty Burridge (Sonoma County), Don Roberson (Monterey County), and Dave Shuford (Marin County).

Once these details were in hand, NSAS formed a Breeding Bird Atlas Steering Committee. A review of historical breeding bird records for both counties was undertaken. Bill Grummer worked on the Napa County list and John Lovio looked for records for Solano County. Old *American Birds* literature was combed, as well as Grinnell and Miller's *Distribution of the Birds of California* and all of the *Pacific Coast Avifauna Journals*. Oologist Emerson Stoner's notes and the notes of Napa and Solano birders were consulted. All of the bird lists for state, county, and city parks were checked as well as every known bird study in both counties. California Department of Fish and Game's records in Yountville and Grizzly Island Wildlife Refuge were researched, as were other available sources of information (see page 185, "Special Sources of Data"). This compilation of records provided a picture of the potential breeding birds of the two counties. Pilot programs for breeding bird atlases began in 1988 for both Napa and Solano Counties. Birders went out with a list of potential breeding birds plus a map describing a 25 square kilometer area (9.65 square miles) and began birding to test what the steering committee had found. Grant money was requested from both the Napa and Solano County Fish and Game Fine Money programs. Napa County provided a $750 grant for Atlas Graphics mapping software, so the Napa-Solano Audubon Society decided to do a breeding bird atlas in Napa.

The NSAS Breeding Bird Atlas Steering Committee organized the effort to cover all of Napa County in search of breeding birds during 1989-1993, using forms it developed. It should be stressed that although the study used AOU standardized methodologies and guidelines, the Napa County Breeding Bird Atlas was organized and primarily produced by volunteers, most of whom had no formal training in ornithology. Individuals who love to watch birds and enjoy Napa's wilder places gathered the data. Lay people, mainly from NSAS but including many others who were not, volunteered countless hours of time.

METHODS

Mapping the County: Maps, Grids, and Blocks

To aid in determining the distribution of breeding birds in the county, a grid system was superimposed on a map of the county. The Universal Transverse Mercator (UTM) grid system was chosen since it had been used by most of the previous atlases in Europe and other counties in California. The UTM system uses metric coordinates and has the advantage of equally sized blocks independent of latitude or longitude. The block size was also one of popular choice, five kilometers (about three miles) square. The maps used were the United States Department of the Interior Geological Survey (USGS) Quadrangles, 7.5 minute series. These maps show 7.5 minutes of latitude and longitude, but they also show 1,000 meter grid ticks for the UTM system. Horizontal and vertical grid lines were drawn on the maps at UTM coordinates ending in 0000 or 5000. Napa County is in UTM zone 10 ranging from 4,223,000-4,302,000 meters N. and 532,000-582,000 meters E. Blocks were numbered using the UTM coordinates of the southwest corner of the block. The block number was generated by listing the east coordinate first, dropping the ending zeroes for each coordinate and dropping the repetitive 4 of the north coordinate; i.e., if the southwest coordinates of a block were 4,235,000 meters N. and 555,000 meters E., then the block number would be 555235. Nowhere did the county boundary coincide with the UTM gridding. Forty-nine of the blocks were judged to be wholly contained within the county. Fifty-five blocks contained some portion of the county. It was decided that for the blocks containing only a part of the county, only the ones comprised of 50% or more would be surveyed. There were thirty blocks in that category. These blocks and the ones wholly contained within the county, a total of seventy-nine, were considered priority blocks. The remaining twenty-five blocks were considered non-priority and were not assigned to atlasers. Anecdotal reports from non-priority blocks were accepted and recorded in a separate database; they do not appear on the atlas maps.

Data Collection Methods

Napa County's Atlas generally used the breeding codes recommended for North American Breeding Bird Atlas Projects by the North American Ornithologists' Atlas Committee (February 1988), with one major exception. The code PE (Physiological evidence of breeding) was deleted, since the bird must be in hand to inspect its brood patch or determine if an egg is in the oviduct.

The breeding categories are ranked as Possible (the least positive evidence), Probable, or Confirmed (the most positive evidence of breeding), with the codes (representing breeding situations/behaviors) listed in order of ascending rank within each category. Only the highest-ranking code was to be reported and has been published in this atlas. Thus a "Z," designating "Species (male or female) observed in suitable nesting habitat during its breeding season," was a lower ranking code within the Possible category than an "X," recording "Singing male in suitable nesting habitat during its breeding season." Refer to Appendix A, Breeding Criteria Codes.

Atlasers were expected to provide dates for all breeding records in the attempt to define the breeding season limits for each species in Napa County.

Conducting the Atlas Fieldwork

A media blitz began in 1988 to inform the community that Napa-Solano Audubon Society (NSAS) was embarking on a five-year study of the breeding birds of Napa County. Napa and Solano County newspapers, local radio stations, and available television channels were contacted. The NSAS newsletter announced the study. Instructional programs on how to "atlas" were held, and an Atlaser's Handbook, patterned after the Sonoma County Breeding Bird Atlas Handbook, was written and distributed at these meetings. Nest boxes were constructed to assist in confirming breeding birds and sold to help fund publication of the Atlas. In the instructional classes, proper birding ethics were emphasized in order to limit possible nest predation. Many field trips were designed to demonstrate these methods while gathering breeding information in a block. A newsletter, *Napa Nest News*, was developed to explain the methodology, as well as to update atlasers on our progress and what remained to be done. Everyone was encouraged to share his or her findings during the breeding season, to share the joy of discovery. First records, of course, needed verification; the atlas steering committee also vetted all unusual breeding records.

NSAS organized 74 volunteers to survey the county for breeding birds between 1989 and 1993. A complete survey was attempted for each priority block in Napa County (those which contained 50% or more of County area). The Atlas Steering Committee debated whether to record fieldwork hours, habitat, and abundance data. It was decided that asking atlasers to record hours in the field might deter volunteers, and, therefore, it was not required. After reflecting on how to record habitat, the steering committee decided against its inclusion. The estimate of abundance was retained for its significance in enabling comparisons of population densities should the Atlas be repeated in the future. However, many atlasers had difficulty assessing abundance and chose not to report it.

Each atlaser was given the *Napa County Breeding Bird Atlas Handbook*, which contained the do's and don'ts of atlasing. It listed the known or potential breeding species of Napa County with short details of courtship, nesting phenology, and a remarks column. Atlasers were encouraged to spend at least two hours at a time in each block and were advised to visit at least twice a month from April through July. They were also asked to sample each of the different habitats within their block. However, in actuality many atlasers went out when they had available time, surveying habitats that were readily accessible or birding on private property when permission could be secured.

METHODS

Volunteers initially chose their priority blocks. Individual blocks were at times surveyed by multiple observers. Usually atlasers visited a single block during a season; toward the end of the project, volunteers were encouraged to survey multiple blocks during the year. Once a block was considered complete (the goal was 50 species per block), the atlaser either chose a new area or was asked to survey an incomplete block. Some blocks were reassigned to the same or other atlasers in subsequent years if coverage was considered incomplete.

Blockbusting

Some blocks were remote from the centers of population or had very few roads. In order to achieve sufficient coverage, it was necessary to hike in or drive in with a four-wheeler and camp. Teams of birders undertook short, intensive birding forays on weekends to gather as much data as possible in several blocks. Atlasers commonly refer to this technique as blockbusting. Where possible, strategic corners of blocks were chosen so that those four blocks could be censused in one day or evening.

Owling and Railing

In every breeding bird atlas, finding owls or birds of the night, such as poorwills, Black-crowned Night-Herons, and most rails, presents a challenge. Special blockbusting techniques were employed for these species. Maps were consulted beforehand for all species but even more closely for rails, since natural and man-made ponds needed to be inventoried. Permission was secured to investigate these special habitats, since most human-made ponds irrigate vineyards or process sanitation district effluent. For owls, knowledge of each species' habitat requirements and permission to survey at night were the keys to successfully finding birds. Sometimes these requirements were met, but then an area might be too noisy because of traffic, a rushing stream, courting frogs or barking dogs. Often only probable and possible evidence was obtained. Given sufficient time and optimum conditions, nocturnal surveys can usually gather confirming evidence (CO). In actual practice, PO (possible) and PR (probable) data represents the nearest atlasers can come to confirmed breeding of several nocturnal species, considering the constraints inherent in the survey.

Casual Observations

A special form, "Birds in Other Areas," was available to report breeding bird behavior anywhere in Napa County outside the confines of individual block assignments. Observers ranging from research biologists to novice birders submitted such information. Reports from inexperienced individuals were critically reviewed, since experience was considered in the decision to accept a report.

Special Sources of Data

Ted Wooster with the California Department of Fish and Game conducted an extensive survey of Spotted Owls in Napa County, and these records were added to the breeding bird Atlas database. He continued the survey after the Atlas period.

Dee Warenycia, Wildlife Biologist with the California Department of Fish and Game's Natural Diversity Data Base (NDDB), assisted the Atlas by providing historic nesting data from the NDDB computerized data base. The NDDB is used to document California's rare and threatened species. Data was translated from their files to breeding codes as appropriate for the Atlas, which, in turn, shared its data with the NDDB.

The Bird Rescue Center of Napa County shared its files. Records were examined and breeding codes established. In many cases the data had to be rejected because locations could not be determined.

The database of the Museum of Vertebrate Zoology of the University of California at Berkeley was reviewed for historic Napa County nesting records. Most were egg records.

Historic egg records of the California Academy of Sciences were searched. Dr. Steve Bailey, the curator of these records, was instrumental in helping provide the Atlas with this data.

Western Museum of Vertebrate Zoology historic records were searched for Napa county eggs. Mr. Lloyd Kiff helped to provide records on individual species. At the time, their records were not computerized, so only searches by species could be made.

The ornithological collection in the Museum at Pacific Union College of Angwin was examined for historical information. Dr. Don Hemphill was instrumental in providing this data.

Data Management

Field cards were to be turned in by September 15 to the Area Coordinator. A Technical Committee screened field cards and "Birds in Other Areas" forms for completeness and inconsistencies. Attempts to adjudicate the records were made, after which Phil Burton entered the data in the first year and Bill Grummer in the remaining four years. Some data was flagged as incomplete. After data entry, each atlaser received a printout of his or her records for review. Highlights and results for the breeding season were published in *Napa Nest News.* Later, Murray Berner performed another review of the breeding records when he wrote the species accounts.

The highest level of breeding information was recorded for each species for the year. If a species was already confirmed for a block, reconfirmation was not required in subsequent years. Because of time constraints for data entry, the Steering Committee decided that once the species was confirmed in a block, no further entries would be made in future years, although continuing breeding evidence or a higher level of confirmed breeding activity might be found.

The Atlas Steering Committee reviewed a table of the full year's results for each block, using a printout of the block's confirmed, probable and possible species, and directed efforts to examine other habitats within priority blocks. The goal was to find at least 50 species per priority block.

RESULTS

Evidence of breeding was recorded for 156 species in Napa County during the Atlas period from 1989-1993. Of these, 145 species (140 native and five introduced) had confirmed breeding records, six species had probable breeding evidence, and five species met the criteria for possible breeding. There was also confirmed breeding evidence for Mandarin Duck, and, after the atlas was completed, for Hermit Warbler.

Database entries were made for 5229 records, resulting in Confirmed 2280 (43.6%), Probable 1408 (26.9%), Possible 1352 (25.8%), and Observed 189 (3.6%).

The average number of species observed per block was 56 in the 79 priority blocks. The highest number of species, 106, was found in block 540265. The lowest number of species, 35, was found in block 555290.

Distribution

The Lesser Goldfinch was the most widely distributed bird, appearing in all of the 79 priority blocks. Species found in 70 or more priority blocks were: Red-tailed Hawk 78, Mourning Dove 78, Turkey Vulture 77, California Quail 77, Western Scrub-Jay 77, California Towhee 77, Nuttall's Woodpecker 76, Oak Titmouse 76, Anna's Hummingbird 75, Acorn Woodpecker 75, Ash-throated Flycatcher 74, Brewer's Blackbird 74, Black-headed Grosbeak 72, Northern Flicker 71, Bushtit 71, Western Bluebird 71, American Robin 71, Bullock's Oriole 71, Black Phoebe 70, European Starling 70, Spotted Towhee 70, and House Finch 70. Napa County contains good habitat for these species, and they are also relatively easy for atlasers to identify, perhaps resulting in more frequent detection than for birds more difficult to identify.

The species that garnered the highest number of confirmed breeding records were Western Scrub-Jay 62, House Finch 59, European Starling 57, Oak Titmouse 56, California Quail 55, California Towhee 55, Western Bluebird 54, Brewer's Blackbird 54, and Bushtit 51.

Of the species above, House Finch had the highest percentage of confirmations vs. all records at 84%. It was closely followed by European Starling 81%, Western Scrub-Jay 80%, and Western Bluebird 76%.

The most widely distributed large wading bird was Green Heron, found in 39 blocks, confirmed in 19. Mallard was the most widely distributed of the waterfowl, seen in 67 blocks, of which 39 were confirmed. Red-tailed Hawk led the diurnal raptors, confirmed in 38 blocks out of 78. Among owls, Barn Owl had the most confirmations, 22 in the 38 blocks where it was found.

Western Screech-Owl was surprisingly the most widely distributed owl, found in 63 blocks, edging out Great Horned Owl, with 61 blocks. It was no surprise that California Quail led the Galliformes in distribution and confirmations, seen in 77 blocks with 55 confirmations. Killdeer led the small wading birds with 29 confirmations in 52 blocks. The most widely distributed woodpecker was Nuttall's Woodpecker; the Picidae with the most confirmations was Acorn Woodpecker in 44 blocks versus Nuttall's in 35 blocks.

The number of species reported in a priority block depends on the biogeography, the observer's birding experience, and the number of survey hours. One priority block was head and shoulders above the rest; Bill Grummer's 540265 block held 106 species, including 76 confirmed. The next highest total was Mike Parmeter's block 555260, with 94 species, 69 confirmed. Block 545260 had 67 confirmations and 550240 had 52. Below is the breakdown of blocks vs. species seen:

Blocks with 100 to 109 species =one
Blocks with 90 to 99 species =one
Blocks with 80 to 89 species =fourteen
Blocks with 70 to 79 species =fourteen
Blocks with 60 to 69 species =twenty-five
Blocks with 50 to 59 species =seventeen
Blocks with 40 to 49 species =five
Blocks with 30 to 39 species =two

The Napa Valley, with its population of birders and easy access, produced more than 70 species per block. Areas in the north near Knoxville, a 1-1/2 hour drive from population centers and with less diversity of habitat, averaged just 45 species per block. The eastern side of Lake Berryessa has excellent biodiversity but is under private ownership, and access to these properties was only available to Napa atlasers during the last year of the Atlas study. The Palisades and Cedar Roughs posed other problems; access was available, but it was a physical challenge to survey this rugged terrain.

CONCLUDING REMARKS

As changes in land use continue, changes in bird populations will follow. Among passerines, House Finch will probably become more widespread with increasing urbanization. Secondary cavity nesters such as Ash-throated Flycatcher and Western Bluebird will decline as suitable cavities are lost to deforestation and habitat fragmentation, although that decline might be slowed by widespread placement of suitable nest boxes. Loggerhead Shrike may be expected to decline severely from habitat loss as open land and pastures are converted to other uses, and Yellow-breasted Chat is unlikely to find the riverine habitat necessary for breeding success. The expansion of Bald Eagle and Peregrine Falcon distribution in Napa County has followed federal protection measures, and water-fowl will benefit from programs developed by Napa's Flood Control District.

The five-year Atlas challenge vastly increased our understanding of Napa County birds and their habitat requirements. Ambitious volunteers turned loose into unexplored regions documented details of distribution previously unknown or described only in the notes of those relatively few amateur ornithologists who dedicated scattered intervals of the 20th century to their favorite patches of the county. The Atlas expanded their work, and its publication has made this vital ecological information available both to the public and to future researchers.

—Robin Leong

Western Kingbird

187

APPENDIX A

Breeding Criteria Codes

DESIGNATION	CODE[1]	EVIDENCE
OBSERVED	O	Species (male or female) **observed** in block during the breeding season, but believed not to be breeding.
POSSIBLE	Z	Species (male or female) observed in suitable nesting habitat during its breeding season.
	X	Singing male present in suitable nesting habitat during its breeding season.
PROBABLE	P	**Pair** observed in suitable nesting habitat during its breeding season.
	S	Permanent territory presumed through **song** at the same location on at least two occasions 7 days or more apart.
	T	Permanent **territory** presumed through defense of territory (chasing individuals of the same species).
	C	**Courtship** behavior or **copulation**.
	N	Visiting probable **nest-site**.
	A	**Agitated** behavior or anxiety calls from adult.
	B	Nest **building** by wrens or excavation of holes by woodpeckers.
CONFIRMED	CN	**Carrying nesting** material, such as sticks or other material.
	NB	**Nest building** by all except woodpeckers and wrens.
	DD	**Distraction display** or injury feigning.
	UN	**Used nest** or eggshells found. Caution: These must be carefully identified, if they are to be accepted.[2]
	PY	Flightless, **precocial young** restricted to the natal area by dependence on adults or limited ability.
	FL	**Recently fledged young** (either precocial or altricial) incapable of sustained flight, restricted to the natal area by dependence on adults or limited mobility.
	ON	Adults entering or leaving a nest site in circumstances indicating **occupied nest**. To be used for nests too high (i.e., the tops of trees) or enclosed (i.e., chimneys) for contents to be seen, or when a tight-sitting adult could be on either eggs or young.
	CF	Adult **carrying food** for the young.
	FY	Adult feeding recently **fledged young**.
	FS	Adult carrying **fecal sac**.
	NE	**Nest** with eggs.[2]
	NY	**Nest** with **young** seen or heard.[2]

[1] The codes in Possible and Probable categories are represented by single letters and in the Confirmed category by double letters. Letters have been selected as a mnemonic aid, keyed to boldfaced words in criteria definitions.

[2] Presence of cowbird eggs or young is confirmation of both cowbird and host species.

APPENDIX B

PART OF AN ATLAS FIELD DATA CARD

<table>
<tr>
<td>

**NAPA COUNTY
BREEDING BIRD ATLAS
FIELD CARD**

Block No._____ Year_____

U.S.G.S. Map_____

Name_____

Address_____

City/Zip_____

Phone_____

* Fill out Unusual Record
Report Form

Return by September 15th
to County Coordinators or
Napa County Breeding Bird Atlas
3601 St. Helena Hwy. N.
Calistoga, CA, 94515

</td>
<td>

BREEDING CODES
OBSERVED:
O-Observed:no evidence of breeding
POSSIBLE:
Z-Species in right habitat in season
X-Singing male present in right hab.
PROBABLE:
P-Pair obverved in right habitat
S-Song in same area; 7 days apart
T-Defense of territory
C-Courtship behavior or copulation
N-Visiting probable nest-site
A-Agitated behavior of adults(s)
B-Wrens building or Woodpeckers
   excavating holes
CONFIRMED:
CN-Carrying nesting material
NB-Nest building at nest site
DD-Distraction display
UN-Used nests or eggshells found
PY-Precocial young; flightless
FL-Fledged young;no sustained.flight
ON-Occupied nest by adults
CF-Carrying food for the young
FY-Adult feeding fledged young
FS-Adult carrying fecal sac
NE-Nest with eggs
NY-Nest with young seen or heard

</td>
</tr>
</table>

SPECIES	O	PO	PR	CO	ABUN	SPECIES	O	PO	PR	CO	ABUN
Pied-billed Grebe						Black-sh. Kite					
Western Grebe						Northern Harrier					
Double-cr. Cormorant						Sharp-shinned Hawk*					
American Bittern*						Cooper's Hawk					
Great Blue Heron						Red-shouldered Hawk					
Great Egret*						Red-tailed Hawk					
Snowy Egret*						Golden Eagle					
Green-backed Heron						American Kestrel					
Black-cr.Night-Heron						Peregrine Falcon*					
Canada Goose						Prairie Falcon*					
Wood Duck						Ring-necked Pheasant					
Mallard						Wild Turkey					
Northern Pintail						California Quail					
Cinnamon Teal						Mountain Quail					
Northern Shoveler*						Black Rail*					
Gadwall						Clapper Rail					
Ruddy Duck*						Virginia Rail					
Turkey Vulture						Sora*					
Osprey						Common Moorhen					

NAPA COUNTY BREEDING BIRD ATLAS
BIRDS IN OTHER AREA FORM

If you observe evidence of a bird breeding in Napa County outside the block you are assigned, please record details on this sheet. If you know who is assigned the block, report your sightings to them to maximize their effort.
Send completed reports to: Bill Grummer, 3601 St. Helena Hwy. N., Calistoga

Species_____Date _____

Observer_____Phone _____

Location (detailed) _____

_____

Block # _____ Breeding Code _____

Comments_____

NAPA COUNTY BREEDING BIRD ATLAS
UNUSUAL RECORD REPORT FORM

Use this form to record details for PRobable or COnfirmed records of asterisked species or species not listed on the BBA Field Card. To facilitate field verification, immediately phone Bill Grummer (942-0136) for sightings north of Oakville or Mike Rippey (224-5409) for sightings south of Oakville.

Species_____ Date_____ Time_____ Reporter_____

Phone_____ Block #_____ USGS Quad_____

Location(detailed)_____

Number, Age & Sex of Individuals_____ Length of Observation_____

 Breeding Behavior Observed_____

_____

How was species identified? (detailed)_____

_____

Nest Location_____

Area Around Nest_____

_____

Equipment Used_____

Other Observers_____ Photographs_____

Tape Recordings_____ Additional information, sketches, maps, etc. (use back of sheet if necessary)

Send the completed form to: Bill Grummer, 3601 St. Helena Hwy. N., Calistoga 94515

APPENDIX C

Monthly Rainfall and Average Temperature
Bothe-Napa Valley State Park
Lat. 38° 32'29", Long. 122° 30'30", Elev. 360'

Rainfall Data From Bothe-Napa Valley State Park
(Season Jul. 1-Jun. 30)

Month	1989 Rain (in.)	1990 Rain (in.)	1991 Rain (in.)	1992 Rain (in.)	1993 Rain (in.)
January	1.52	8.19	0.87	2.38	17.79
February	1.4	4.99	4.82	12.26	9.08
March	13.11	1.68	20.66	5.97	2.81
April	1.52	0.3	0.45	1.38	2.1
May	0.15	3.48	0.43	0	1.92
June	0.26	0	0.66	1.33	1.17
Season Total	**31.04**	**27.09**	**30.37**	**31.17**	**52.89**
July	0	0	0.01	0	0
August	0	0	0.15	0	0
September	1.86	0.18	0	0	0
October	5.2	0.68	2.26	4.06	1.53
November	1.34	0.61	1.75	.91	4
December	0.05	1.01	3.68	13.05	5.98

Average High Temperatures at
Bothe-Napa Valley State Park (F.)

Month	1989	1990	1991	1992	1993
January	53.1	77.9	56.5	53	51.2
February	53.6	54.5	63.2	59.8	55
March	60.4	63.8	57.5	62.8	66.8
April	72.6	72.1	68.1	71.7	67.8
May	73.7	M	73.9	82.1	74.4
June	81.8	83	81.8	80.9	82.5
July	90.1	88.8	87.6	85.8	87.6
August	84.9	86.8	83.2	90.1	88
September	M	83	81.7	82.7	84.9
October	70.2	76	80	74.8	72.8
November	62.8	62.2	62	62.5	62
December	52.7	50.2	54.6	50.7	M

Average Low Temperatures at
Bothe-Napa Valley State Park (F.)

Month	1989	1990	1991	1992	1993
January	34.4	50.5	35.8	35	37.3
February	35.1	35.8	41.7	44.5	40.8
March	44.2	41.1	40	44.6	46.7
April	47.3	48	43.1	46.8	45.6
May	47.9	M	46.9	53.3	51.9
June	54.1	53.2	49.9	54.7	52.7
July	53.8	57.1	55.6	56.3	56.5
August	54.7	57.1	54.5	55.4	56.8
September	M	53.1	53.3	53	53.6
October	47.6	44.5	47.6	51.4	51.7
November	41.3	39.9	43	41.9	41.3
December	34.3	30.3	37	36.4	M

REFERENCES

Altman, B. and R. Sallabanks. 2000. "Olive-sided Flycatcher." *The Birds of North America, No. 502.* A. Poole and F. Gill, Eds. The Birds of North America, Inc., Philadelphia, PA.

Ammon, E.M. and W.M. Gilbert. 1999. "Wilson's Warbler." *The Birds of North America, No. 478.* A. Poole and F. Gill, Eds. The Birds of North America, Inc., Philadelphia, PA.

Arnold, T.W. 1993. "Factors affecting renesting in American Coots." *Condor 95:273-281.*

Austin, J.E. and M.R. Miller. 1995. "Northern Pintail." *The Birds of North America, No. 163.* A. Poole and F. Gill, Eds. The Academy of Natural Sciences, Philadelphia, PA, and The American Ornithologists' Union, Washington, D.C.

Austin, J.E., C.M. Custer, and A.D. Afton. 1998. "Lesser Scaup." *The Birds of North America, No. 338.* A. Poole and F. Gill, Eds. The Birds of North America, Inc., Philadelphia, PA.

Austin, O.L., Jr., Ed. "Life histories of North American cardinals, grosbeaks, buntings, towhees, finches, sparrows, and allies." *U.S. Natl. Mus. Bull. 237.*

Baicich, P.J. and C.J.O. Harrison. 1997. *A guide to the nests, eggs, and nestlings of North American birds.* San Diego: Academic Press.

Bailey, S.F., R.A. Erickson, and D.G. Yee. 1989. "The nesting season, Middle Pacific Coast region." *Am Birds 43:1362-1366.*

Bailey, S.F., D.G. Yee, and B.E. Deuel. 1992. "Middle Pacific Coast Region." *Am Birds 46:1173-1176.*

Baylands ecosystem habitat goals: a report of habitat recommendations / prepared by the San Francisco Bay Area Wetlands Ecosystem Goals Project. 1999. San Francisco Estuary Project c/o S.F. Bay Regional Water Quality Control Board. Oakland, CA.

Beedy, E.C. and W.J. Hamilton III. 1999. "Tri-colored Blackbird." *The Birds of North America, No. 423.* A. Poole and F. Gill, Eds. The Birds of North America, Inc., Philadelphia, PA.

Bemis, C. and J.D. Rising. 1999. "Western Wood-Pewee." *The Birds of North America, No. 451.* A. Poole and F. Gill, Eds. The Birds of North America, Inc., Philadelphia, PA.

Bent, A.C. 1923. "Life histories of North American wild fowl." vol. 1. *U.S. Natl. Mus. Bull. 126.*

_____. 1925. "Life histories of North American wild fowl." vol. 2. *U.S. Natl. Mus. Bull. 130.*

_____. 1926. "Life histories of North American marsh birds." *U.S. Natl. Mus. Bull. 135.*

_____. 1929. "Life histories of North American shore birds." vol. 2. *U.S. Natl. Mus. Bull. 146.*

_____. 1932. "Life histories of North American gallinaceous birds." *U.S. Natl. Mus. Bull. 162.*

_____. 1938. "Life histories of North American birds of prey." vol. 2. *U.S. Natl. Mus. Bull. 170.*

_____. 1939. "Life histories of North American woodpeckers." *U.S. Natl. Mus. Bull. 174.*

_____. 1940. "Life histories of North American cuckoos, goatsuckers, hummingbirds, and their allies," vol.2. *U.S. Natl. Mus. Bull. 176.*

_____. 1942. "Life histories of North American flycatchers, larks, swallows, and their allies." *U.S. Natl. Mus. Bull. 179.*

_____. 1946. "Life histories of North American jays, crows, and titmice." *U.S. Natl. Mus. Bull. 191.*

_____. 1948. "Life histories of North American nuthatches, wrens, thrashers, and their allies." *U.S. Natl. Mus. Bull. 195.*

_____. 1949. "Life histories of North American thrushes, kinglets, and their allies." *U.S. Natl. Mus. Bull. 196.*

_____. 1950. "Life histories of North American wagtails, shrikes, vireos, and their allies." *U.S. Natl. Mus. Bull. 197.*

_____. 1958. "Life histories of North American blackbirds, orioles, tanagers, and allies." *U.S. Natl. Mus. Bull. 211.*

Bickford, E.L. 1932. "The wood ducks of Napa County, California." *Condor 34:101.*

Bloom, P.H. and S.J. Hawks. 1983. "Nest box use and reproductive biology of the American kestrel in Lassen County, California." *Raptor Research 17:9-14.*

Boarman, W.I. and B. Heinrich. 1999. "Common Raven." *The Birds of North America, no. 476.* A. Poole and F. Gill, Eds. The Birds of North America, Inc., Philadelphia, PA.

Boyce, D.A. Jr., R.L. Garrett, and B.J. Walton. 1986. "Distribution and density of prairie falcons in California during the 1970s." *Raptor Research 20:71-74.*

Brown, C.R. and M.B. Brown. 1995. "Cliff Swallow." *The Birds of North America, No. 149.* A. Poole and F. Gill, Eds. The Academy of Natural Sciences, Philadelphia, PA, and the American Ornithologists' Union, Washington, D.C.

Brown, C.R. and M.B. Brown. 1999. "Barn Swallow." *The Birds of North America, No. 452.* A. Poole and F. Gill, Eds. The Birds of North America, Inc., Philadelphia, PA.

Buehler, D.A. 2000. "Bald Eagle." *The Birds of North America, No. 506.* A. Poole and F. Gill, Eds. The Birds of North America, Inc., Philadelphia, PA.

Bull, E.L. and J.A. Jackson. 1995. "Pileated Woodpecker." *The Birds of North America, No. 148.* A. Poole and F. Gill, Eds. The Academy of Natural Sciences, Philadelphia, PA, and The American Ornithologists' Union, Washington, D.C.

Burridge, Betty, ed. 1995. *Sonoma County Breeding Bird Atlas.* Madrone Audubon Society, Santa Rosa, CA.

Butler, R. W. 1992. "Great Blue Heron." *The Birds of North America, No. 25.* A. Poole, P. Stettenheim, and F. Gill, Eds. The Academy of Natural Sciences, Philadelphia, PA, and The American Ornithologists' Union, Washington, D.C.

REFERENCES

California State Association of Counties web site. http://www.csac.counties.org. 2003. Sacramento, CA.

California State Resources Agency web site. http://www.resources.ca.gov. 2003. Sacramento, CA.

Calkins, J.D., J.C. Hagelin, and D.F. Lott. 1999. "California Quail." *The Birds of North America, No. 473.* A. Poole and F. Gill, Eds. The Birds of North America, Inc., Philadelphia, PA.

Campbell, K.F., R.E. Erickson, and S.F. Bailey. 1985. "The nesting season, Middle Pacific Coast Region." *Am Birds 39:956-961.*

Cannings, R.J. 1993. "Northern Saw-whet Owl." *The Birds of North America, No.42.* A. Poole and F. Gill, Eds. The Academy of Natural Sciences, Philadelphia, PA, and the American Ornithologists' Union, Washington, D.C.

Cardiff, S.W. and D. L. Dittmann. 2002. "Ash-throated Flycatcher." *The Birds of North America, No. 664.* A. Poole and F. Gill, Eds. The Birds of North America, Inc., Philadelphia, PA.

Checklist of North American Birds. 1983. 6th ed. American Ornithologists' Union, Washington, D.C.

Checklist of North American Birds. 1998. 7th ed. American Ornithologists' Union, Washington, D.C.

Childs, H.E., Jr., 1968. "San Francisco Brown Towhee." Grinnell and Swarth, pp.605-615. "Life histories of North American cardinals, grosbeaks, buntings, towhees, finches, sparrows, and allies." O.L. Austin, Jr., Ed. *U.S. Natl. Mus. Bull. 237.*

Chu, M. and G. Walsberg. 1999. "Phainopepla." *The Birds of North America, No. 415.* A. Poole and F. Gill, Eds. The Birds of North America, Inc., Philadelphia, PA.

Cicero, C. 2000. "Oak Titmouse." *The Birds of North America, No. 485.* A. Poole and F. Gill, Eds. The Birds of North America, Inc., Philadelphia, PA.

Clark, H.W. 1930. "Notes on the avifauna of a Transition Island in Napa County, California." *Condor 32:50-52.*

Cody, M.L. 1998. "California Thrasher." *The Birds of North America, No. 323.* A. Poole and F. Gill, Eds. The Birds of North America, Inc., Philadelphia, PA.

Collins, P.W. 1999. "Rufous-crowned Sparrow." *The Birds of North America, No. 472.* A. Poole and F. Gill, Eds. The Birds of North America, Inc., Philadelphia, PA.

Cuthbert, F.J. and L.R. Wires. 1999. "Caspian Tern." *The Birds of North America, No. 403.* A. Poole and F. Gill, Eds. The Birds of North America, Inc., Philadelphia, PA.

Davis, J.N. 1995. "Hutton's Vireo." *The Birds of North America, No. 189.* A. Poole and F. Gill, Eds. The Academy of Natural Sciences, Philadelphia, PA, and The American Ornithologists' Union, Washington, D.C.

Davis, J.N. 1999. "Lawrence's Goldfinch." *The Birds of North America, No. 480.* A. Poole and F. Gill, Eds. The Birds of North America, Inc., Philadelphia, PA.

Davis, W.E., Jr., 1993. "Black-crowned Night-Heron." *The Birds of North America, No. 74.* A. Poole and F. Gill, Eds. The Academy of Natural Sciences, Philadelphia, PA, and The American Ornithologists' Union, Washington, D.C.

Davis, W.E., Jr., and J.A. Kushlan. 1994. "Green Heron." *The Birds of North America, No. 129.* A. Poole and F. Gill, Eds. The Academy of Natural Sciences, Philadelphia, PA, and The American Ornithologists' Union, Washington, D.C.

DeJong, M.J. 1996. "Northern Rough-winged Swallow." *The Birds of North America, No. 234.* A. Poole and F. Gill, Eds. The Academy of Natural Sciences, Philadelphia, PA, and The American Ornithologists' Union, Washington, D.C.

DeSante, D.F., E. Ruhlen, S. Amin, and K.M. Burton. 1993. "Results of a 1991 census of burrowing owls in Central California: an alarmingly small and declining population." The Institute for Bird Populations. Abstracts of presentations made at the annual meeting of the Raptor Research Foundation, Inc. *Journal of Raptor Research 27:53-96*

Dubowy, P.J. 1996. "Northern Shoveler." *The Birds of North America, No. 217.* A. Poole and F. Gill, Eds. The Academy of Natural Sciences, Philadelphia, PA, and the American Ornithologists' Union, Washington, D.C.

Dunk, J.R. 1995. "White-tailed Kite." *The Birds of North America, No. 178.* A. Poole and F. Gill, Eds. The Academy of Natural Sciences, Philadelphia, PA, and The American Ornithologists' Union, Washington, DC.

Dunn, J. and K. Garrett. 1997. *A field guide to warblers of North America.* Boston: Houghton Mifflin.

Eddleman, W.R., R.E. Flores, and M.L. Legare. 1994. "Black Rail." *The Birds of North America, No. 123.* A. Poole and F. Gill, Eds. The Academy of Natural Sciences, Philadelphia, PA, and The American Ornithologists' Union, Washington, D.C.

Eddleman, W.R. and C.J. Conway. 1998. "Clapper Rail." *The Birds of North America, No. 340.* A. Poole and F. Gill, Eds. The Birds of North America, Inc., Philadelphia, PA.

Ellison, W.G. 1992. "Blue-gray Gnatcatcher." *The Birds of North America, No. 23.* A. Poole, P. Stettenheim, and F. Gill, Eds. The Academy of Natural Sciences, Philadelphia, PA, and The American Ornithologists' Union, Washington, D.C.

Erickson, M.M. 1948. "Gambel's Wrentit." pp. 81-83. "Life histories of North American nuthatches, wrens, thrashers, and their allies." A.C. Bent, Ed. *U.S. Natl. Mus. Bull. 195.*

Erickson, R.A., S.F. Bailey, and D.G. Yee. 1989. "Middle Pacific Coast Region." *Am Birds 43:531-535.*

REFERENCES

Evens, J.G., G.W. Page, S.A. Laymon, and R.W. Stallcup. 1991. "Distribution, relative abundance, and status of the California Black Rail in Western North America." *Condor 93:952-966.*

Feltes, C.H. 1936. "Trapping Cedar Waxwings in the San Joaquin Valley, California." *Condor 38:18-23.*

Ferguson-Lees, J. and D.A. Christie. 2001. *Raptors of the world.* Boston: Houghton Mifflin.

Field Guide to the Birds of North America. 1999. 3rd ed. National Geographic Society, Washington, D.C.

Fisher, W.K. 1900. "A list of birds observed on Mt. St. Helena, California." *Condor 2:135-138.*

Fowler, F.H. 1931. "Studies of food and growth of the prairie falcon." *Condor 33:193-201.*

Gammonley, J.H. 1996. "Cinnamon Teal." *The Birds of North America, No. 209.* A. Poole and F. Gill, Eds. The Academy of Natural Sciences, Philadelphia, PA, and The American Ornithologists' Union, Washington, D.C.

Gardali, T. and G. Ballard. 2000. "Warbling Vireo." *The Birds of North America, No. 551.* A. Poole and F. Gill, Eds. The Birds of North America, Inc., Philadelphia, PA.

Ghalambor, C. and T.E. Martin. 1999. "Red-breasted Nuthatch." *The Birds of North America, No. 459.* A. Poole and F. Gill, Eds. The Birds of North America, Inc., Philadelphia, PA.

Gill, R.E., Jr., and R. Mewaldt. 1983. "Pacific Coast Caspian Terns: dynamics of an expanding population." *Auk 100:319-381.*

Gill, Robert Jr. 1977. "Breeding avifauna of the South San Francisco Bay Estuary." *Western Birds 8:1-8.*

Giudice, J.H. and J.T. Ratti. 2001. "Ring-necked Pheasant." *The Birds of North America, No. 572.* A. Poole and F. Gill, Eds. The Birds of North America, Inc., Philadelphia, PA.

Goguen, C.B. and D.R. Curson, 2002. "Cassin's Vireo." *The Birds of North America, No. 615.* A. Poole and F. Gill, Eds. The Birds of North America, Inc., Philadelphia, PA.

Greene, E., V.R. Muehter, and W. Davison. 1996. "Lazuli Bunting." *The Birds of North America, No. 232.* A. Poole and F. Gill, Eds. The Academy of Natural Sciences, Philadelphia, PA, and The American Ornithologists' Union, Washington, D.C.

Greene, E., W. Davison, and V.R. Muehter. 1998. "Steller's Jay." *The Birds of North America, No. 343.* A. Poole and F. Gill, Eds. The Birds of North America, Inc., Philadelphia, PA.

Greenlaw, J.S. 1996. "Spotted Towhee." *The Birds of North America, No. 263.* A. Poole and F. Gill, Eds. The Academy of Natural Sciences, Philadelphia, PA, and The American Ornithologists' Union, Washington, D.C.

Grinnell, J. and M.W. Wythe. 1927. "Directory to the bird-life of the San Francisco Bay region." *Pacific Coast Avifauna, No. 18.*

_____. and A.H. Miller. 1944. "The distribution of the birds of California." *Pacific Coast Avifauna, No. 27.*

Grummer, W.T., R.L.C. Leong, and M.F. Rippey. 1990. *Napa County breeding bird atlas handbook.* Napa-Solano Audubon Society, Vallejo, California.

Guinan, J.A., P.A. Gowaty, and E.K. Eltzroth. 2000. "Western Bluebird." *The Birds of North America, No. 510.* A. Poole and F. Gill, Eds. The Birds of North America, Inc., Philadelphia, PA.

Gutierrez, R.J. and D.J. Delehanty. 1999. "Mountain Quail." *The Birds of North America, No. 457.* A. Poole and F. Gill, Eds. The Birds of North America, Inc., Philadelphia, PA.

Guzy, M.J. and G. Ritchison. 1999. "Common Yellowthroat." *The Birds of North America, No. 448.* A. Poole and F. Gill, Eds. The Birds of North America, Inc., Philadelphia, PA.

Harrap, S. and D. Quinn. 1995. *Chickadees, tits, nuthatches, and treecreepers.* Princeton: Princeton University Press.

Hatch, J.J. and D.V. Weseloh. 1999. "Double-crested Cormorant." *The Birds of North America, No. 441.* A. Poole and F. Gill, Eds. The Birds of North America, Inc., Philadelphia, PA.

Hejl, S.J., J.A. Holmes, and D.E. Kroodsma. 2002. "Winter Wren." *The Birds of North America, No. 623.* A. Poole and F. Gill, Eds. The Birds of North America, Inc., Philadelphia, PA.

Herman, S.G. 1971. "The peregrine falcon decline in California II. Breeding status in 1970." *Am Birds 25:818-820.*

Hill, G.E. 1993. "House Finch." *The Birds of North America, No. 46.* A. Poole and F. Gill, Eds. The Academy of Natural Sciences, Philadelphia, PA, and The American Ornithologists' Union, Washington, D.C.

Hill, G.E. 1995. "Black-headed Grosbeak." *The Birds of North America, No. 143.* A. Poole and F. Gill, Eds. The Academy of Natural Sciences, Philadelphia, PA, and The American Ornithologists' Union, Washington, D.C.

Hobson, Kathy, P. Perrine, E. Roberts, M. Foster and P. Woodin. 1986. "Breeding season survey of salt marsh yellowthroats in the San Francisco Bay Region." Rev. 1986. Contract No. 84-57. Prepared for U.S. Fish and Wildlife Service. San Francisco Bay Bird Observatory.

Hoffman, R. 1927. *Birds of the Pacific States.* Boston: Houghton Mifflin.

Holt, D.W. and J.L. Petersen. 2000. "Northern Pygmy-Owl." *The Birds of North America, No. 494.* A. Poole and F. Gill, Eds. The Birds of North America, Inc., Philadelphia, PA.

Houston, C.S., D.G. Smith, and C. Rohner. "Great-horned Owl." *The Birds of North America, No. 372.* A. Poole and F. Gill, Eds. The Academy of Natural Sciences, Philadelphia, PA, and The American Ornithologists' Union, Washington, D.C.

Hughes, J.M. "Greater Roadrunner." *The Birds of North America, No. 244.* A. Poole and F. Gill, Eds. The Academy of Natural Sciences, Philadelphia, PA, and The American Ornithologists' Union, Washington, D.C.

Hull, C.N. 1989. "Additional pine siskin nesting records for southern Michigan." *Jack-Pine Warbler 67:131-133.*

REFERENCES

Jackson, B.J.S. and J.A. Jackson. 2000. "Killdeer." *The Birds of North America, No. 517*. A. Poole and F. Gill, Eds. The Birds of North America, Inc., Philadelphia, PA.

Jackson, J.A. and H.R. Ouellet. 2002. "Downy Woodpecker." *The Birds of North America, No. 613*. A. Poole and F. Gill, Eds. The Birds of North America, Inc., Philadelphia, PA.

Jaramillo, A. and P. Burke. 1999. *New World Blackbirds: the Icterids*. Princeton: Princeton University Press.

Jarman, W.M., S.A. Burns, C.E. Bacon, J. Rechtin, S. DeBenedetti, J.L. Linthicum, and B.J. Walton. 1996. "High levels of HCB and DDE associated with reproductive failure in prairie falcons (Falco mexicanus) from California." *Bulletin of Environmental Contamination and Toxicology 57:8-15*.

Jenkins, J.M., R.E. Jackman, and W.G. Hunt. 1999. "Survival and movements of immature bald eagles fledged in Northern California." *Journal of Raptor Research 33:81-86*.

Johnson, L.S. 1998. "House Wren." *The Birds of North America, No. 380*. A. Poole and F. Gill, Eds. The Birds of North America, Inc., Phadelphia, PA.

Johnson, R.F. 1992. "Rock Dove." *The Birds of North America, No. 13*. A. Poole, P. Stettenheim, and F. Gill, Eds. The Academy of Natural Sciences, Philadelphia, PA, and the American Ornithologists' Union, Washington, D.C.

Johnson, R.R. 1968. "Western Chipping Sparrow." pp.1184-85. "Life histories of North American cardinals, grosbeaks, buntings, towhees, finches, sparrows, and allies." O.L. Austin, Jr., Ed. *U.S. Natl. Mus. Bull. 237*.

Jones, P.W. and T.M. Donovan. 1996. "Hermit Thrush." *The Birds of North America, No. 261*. A. Poole and F. Gill, Eds. The Academy of Natural Sciences, Philadelphia, PA, and The American Ornithologists' Union, Washington, D.C.

Jones, S.L. and J.S. Dieni. 1955. "Canyon Wren." *The Birds of North America, No. 197*. A. Poole and F. Gill, Eds. The Academy of Natural Sciences, Phildelphia, PA, and The American Ornithologists' Union, Washington, D.C.

Kelly, J., H.M. Pratt, and P.L. Green. 1993. "The distribution, reproductive success, and habitat characteristics of heron and egret breeding colonies in the San Francisco Bay Area." *Colonial Waterbirds 16:18-27*.

Kennedy, E.D. and D.W. White. 1997. "Bewick's Wren." *The Birds of North America, No. 315*. A. Poole and F. Gill, Eds. The Academy of Natural Sciences, Philadelphia, PA, and The American Ornithologists' Union, Washington, D.C.

Keppie, D.M. and C.E. Braun. 2000. "Band-tailed Pigeon." *The Birds of North America, No. 530*. A. Poole and F. Gill, Eds. The Birds of North America, Inc., Philadelphia, PA.

Kingery, H.E. 1996. "American Dipper." *The Birds of North America, No. 229*. A. Poole and G. Gill, Eds. The Academy of Natural Sciences, Philadelphia, PA, and The American Ornithologists' Union, Washington, D.C.

Kingery, H.E. and C.K. Ghalambor. 2001. "Pygmy Nuthatch." *The Birds of North America No. 567*. A. Poole and F. Gill, Eds. The Birds of North America, Inc., Philadelphia, PA.

Kirk, D.A. and M.J. Mossman. 1998. "Turkey Vulture." *The Birds of North America, No. 339*. A. Poole and F. Gill, Eds. The Birds of North America, Inc., Philadelphia, PA.

Knight, R.L. 1984. "Response of nesting ravens to people in areas of different human densities." *Condor 86:345-346*.

_____, D.L. Grout, and S.A. Temple. 1987. "Nest defense behavior of the American crow in urban and rural areas." *Condor 89:175-177*.

Koenig, W.D., P.B. Stacey, M.T. Stanback, and R.L. Mumme. "Acorn Woodpecker." *The Birds of North America, No. 194*. A. Poole and F. Gill, Eds. The Academy of Natural Sciences, Philadelphia, PA, and The American Ornithologists' Union, Washington, D.C.

Kortright, F.H. 1953. *The ducks, geese, and swans of North America*. Harrisburg: The Stackpole Co.

Kroodsma, D.E. and J. Verner. 1997. "Marsh Wren." *The Birds of North America, No. 308*. A. Poole and F. Gill, Eds. The Academy of Natural Sciences, Philadelphia, PA, and The American Ornithologists' Union, Washington, D.C.

Lambert, G. and J. Kashiwagi. 1978. *Soil Survey of Napa County, California*. U.S. Dept. of Agriculture. Soil Conservation Service.

Leschack, S.K., S.K. McKnight, and G.R. Hepp. 1997. "Gadwall." *The Birds of North America, No. 283*. A. Poole and F. Gill, Eds. The Academy of Natural Sciences, Philadelphia, PA, and The American Ornithologists' Union, Washington, D.C.

Linsdale, J.M. 1937. "The natural history of magpies." *Pacfic Coast Avifauna, No. 25*.

_____. 1968. "Green-backed goldfinch." pp.474-486. "Life histories of North American cardinals, grosbeaks, buntings, towhees, finches, sparrows, and allies." O.L. Austin, Jr., Ed. *U.S. Natl. Mus. Bull. 237*.

Longhurst, W.L. 1959. "An unusual concentration of white-tailed kites in Napa County, California." *Condor 61:301*.

Lowther, P.E. 1993. "Brown-headed Cowbird." *The Birds of North America, No. 47*. A. Poole and F. Gill, Eds. The Academy of Natural Sciences, Philadelphia, PA, and American Ornithologists' Union, Washington, D.C.

_____. 2000. "Nuttall's Woodpecker." *The Birds of North America, No. 555.* A. Poole and F. Gill, Eds. The Birds of North America, Inc., Philadelphia, PA.

_____. 2000. "Pacific-slope Flycatcher." *The Birds of North America, No. 556.* A. Poole and F. Gill, Eds. The Birds of North America, Inc., Philadelphia, PA.

Mack, D.E. and W. Yong. 2000. "Swainson's Thrush." *The Birds of North America, No. 540.* A. Poole and F. Gill, Eds. The Birds of North America, Inc., Philadelphia, PA.

MacWhirter, R. Bruce and K. Bildstein. 1996. "Northern Harrier." *The Birds of North America, No. 210.* A. Poole and F. Gill, Eds. The Academy of Natural Sciences, Philadelphia, PA, and The American Ornithologists' Union, Washington, D.C.

Mallory, M. and K. Metz. 1999. "Common Merganser." *The Birds of North America, No. 442.* The Birds of North America, Inc., Philadelphia, PA.

Marks, J.S., D.L. Evans, and D.W. Holt. 1994. "Long-eared Owl." *The Birds of North America, No. 133.* A. Poole and F. Gill, Eds. The Academy of Natural Sciences, Philadelphia, PA, and The American Ornithologists' Union, Washington, D.C.

Marshall, J.T., Jr. 1948. "Ecologic races of song sparrows in the San Francisco Bay region, Part I, habitat and abundance." *Condor 50:193-215.*

_____. 1948. "Ecologic races of song sparrows in the San Francisco Bay region, Part II, geographic variation." *Condor 50:233-266.*

Marti, C.D. 1992. "Barn Owl." *The Birds of North America, No. 1.* A Poole, P. Stettenheim, and F. Gill, Eds. The Academy of Natural Sciences, Philadelphia, PA, and The American Ornithologists' Union, Washington, D.C.

Martin, S.G. 2002. "Brewer's Blackbird." *The Birds of of North America, No. 616.* A. Poole and F. Gill, Eds. The Birds of North America, Inc., Philadelphia, PA.

Martin, S.M. and J.P. Gibbs. 1996. "Sora." *The Birds of North America, No. 250.* A. Poole and F. Gill, Eds. The Academy of Natural Sciences, Philadelphia, PA, and The American Ornithologists' Union, Washington, D.C.

McNicholl, M.K. P.E. Lowther, and J.A. Hall. 2001. "Forster's Tern." *The Birds of North America, No. 595.* A. Poole and F. Gill, Eds. The Birds of North America, Inc., Philadelphia, PA.

Middleton, A.L.A. 1993. "American Goldfinch." *The Birds of North America, No. 80.* A. Poole and F. Gill, Eds. The Academy of Natural Sciences, Philadelphia, PA, and The American Ornithologists' Union, Washington, D.C.

Mirarchi, R.E. and T.S. Baskett. 1994. "Mourning Dove." *The Birds of North America, No. 117.* A. Poole and F. Gill, Eds. The Academy of Natural Sciences, Philadelphia, PA, and The American Ornithologists' Union, Washington, D.C.

Mitchell, D.E. 2000. "Allen's Hummingbird." *The Birds of North America, No. 501.* A. Poole and F. Gill, Eds. The Birds of North America, Inc., Philadelphia, PA.

Mowbray, T.B. 2002. "Canvasback." *The Birds of North America, No. 659.* A. Poole and F. Gill, Eds. The Birds of North America, Inc., Philadelphia, PA.

Muller, M.J. and R.W. Storer. 1999. "Pied-billed Grebe." *The Birds of North America, No. 410.* A. Poole and F. Gill, Eds. The Birds of North America, Inc., Philadelphia, PA.

Napa County Board of Supervisors. 2000. *Napa River Watershed Phase II Final Report.* Napa, CA.

Napa County, California, web site. http://www.co.napa.ca.us. 2003. Napa, CA.

Napa County Conservation, Development and Planning Dept. *Napa County Environmental Sensitivity Maps. 2002.* Napa County, CA.

Napa County General Plan. 1983 and amendments through 1992. Board of Supervisors. Napa County, CA.

Norris, R.A. 1958. "Comparative biosystematics and life history of the nuthatches Sitta pygmaea and Sitta pusilla. *University of California Publications in Zoology 56:119-300.*

Norris, Robert M. and Robert W. Webb. 1990. 2nd ed. *Geology of California.* New York: John Wiley and Sons, Inc.

Nur, N. and H. Spautz. 2002. "Tidal marsh song sparrows of San Francisco Bay, significant findings". *Observer No. 128, p.2.*

Oring, L.W., E.M. Gray, and J.M. Reed. 1997. "Spotted Sandpiper." *The Birds of North America, No. 289.* A. Poole and F. Gill, Eds. The Academy of Natural Sciences, Philadelphia, PA, and The American Ornithologists Union, Washington, D.C.

Page, G.W. and L.E. Stenzel. 1981. "The breeding status of the snowy plover in California." *Western Birds 12:1-40.*

Page, G.W., J.S. and J.C. Warriner, and P.W.C. Paton. 1995. "Snowy Plover." *The Birds of North America, No. 154.* A. Poole and F. Gill, Eds. The Academy of Natural Sciences, Philadelphia, PA, and The American Ornithologists' Union, Washington, D.C.

Palmer, R.S. 1968. "Pine Siskin." pp.424-447. "Life histories of North American cardinals, grosbeaks, buntings, towhees, finches, sparrows, and allies." O.L. Austin, Jr., Ed. *U.S. Natl. Mus. Bull. 237.*

_____. Ed. 1976. *Handbook of North American Birds, vol. 3.* New Haven: Yale University Press.

Pardieck, K.L. and J.R. Sauer. 2000. "The 1995-1999 summary of the North American breeding bird survey." *Bird Populations 5:30-48.*

Phelps, J.H., Jr. 1968. "Oregon Junco." pp.1050-1071. "Life histories of North American cardinals, grosbeaks, buntings, towhees, finches, sparrows, and allies." O.L. Austin, Jr., Ed. *U.S. Natl. Mus. Bull. 237.*

REFERENCES

Pitocchelli, J. 1995. "MacGillivray's Warbler." *The Birds of North America, No. 159.* A. Poole and F. Gill, Eds. The Academy of Natural Sciences, Philadelphia, PA, and The American Ornithologists' Union, Washington, D.C.

Platt, J.B. 1974. "Sharp-shinned hawk nesting and nest site selection in Utah." *Condor 78:102-103.*

Point Reyes Bird Observatory. 1999. "San Francisco Bay project." *Observer No. 118, pp.8-10.*

Pradosudov, V.V. and T.C. Grubb, Jr. 1993. "White-breasted Nuthatch." *The Birds of North America, No. 54.* A. Poole and F. Gill, Eds. The Academy of Natural Sciences, Philadelphia, PA, and The American Ornithologists' Union, Washington, D.C.

Preston, C.R. and R.D. Beane. 1993. "Red-tailed Hawk." *The Birds of North America, No. 52.* A. Poole, P. Stettenheim, and F.Gill, Eds. The Academy of Natural Sciences, Philadelphia, PA, and The American Ornithologists' Union, Washington, D.C.

Reynolds, M.D. 1995. "Yellow-billed Magpie." *The Birds of North America, No. 180.* A. Poole and F. Gill, Eds. The Academy of Natural Sciences, Philadelphia, PA, and The American Ornithologists' Union, Washington, D.C.

Rippey, Karen E. 2002. *Napa River Watershed Habitat Assessment.* Unpublished report. U.S. Army Corps of Engineers. San Francisco, CA.

Rising, J.D. and P.L. Williams. 1999. "Bullock's Oriole." *The Birds of North America, No. 416.* A. Poole and F. Gill, Eds. The Birds of North America, Inc., Philadelphia, PA.

Roberson, D. and C. Tenney, Eds. 1993. *Atlas of the breeding birds of Monterey County, California.* Monterey Peninsula Audubon Society, Carmel, California.

Robinson, J.A., L.W. Oring, J.P. Skorupa, and R. Boettcher. 1997. "American Avocet." *The Birds of North America, No. 275.* A. Poole and F. Gill, Eds. The Academy of Natural Sciences, Philadelphia, PA, and The American Ornithologists' Union, Washington, D.C.

Robinson, J.A., J.M. Reed, J.P. Skorupa, and L.W. Oring. 1999. "Black-necked Stilt." *The Birds of North America, No. 449.* A. Poole and F. Gill, Eds. The Birds of North America, Inc., Philadelphia, PA.

Rohwer, F.C., W.P. Johnson, and E.R. Loos. 2002. "Blue-winged Teal." *The Birds of North America, No. 625.* A. Poole and F. Gill, Eds. The Birds of North America, Inc., Philadelphia, PA.

Rosenfeld, R.N. and J. Bielefelt. 1993. "Cooper's Hawk." *The Birds of North America, No. 75.* A. Poole and F. Gill, Eds. The Academy of Natural Sciences, Philadelphia, PA, and The American Ornithologists' Union, Washington, D.C.

Russell, S.M. 1996. "Anna's Hummingbird." *The Birds of North America, No. 226.* A. Poole and F. Gill, Eds. The Academy of Natural Sciences, Philadelphia, PA, and The American Ornithologists' Union, Washington, D.C.

Ryan, T.P. and C.T. Collins. 2000. "White-throated Swift." *The Birds of North America, No. 526.* A. Poole and F. Gill, Eds. The Birds of North America, Inc., Philadelphia, PA.

Salyer, J.C. and K.F. Lagler. 1946. "The Eastern Belted Kingfisher Megaceryle alcyon alcyon (Linnaeus) in relation to fish management." *Trans. Am. Fish. Soc. 76:97-117.*

Sauer, J.R., J.E. Hines, and J. Fuller. "The North American Breeding Bird Survey, Results and Analysis 1966-2000. Version 2001-2." *USGS Patuxent Wildlife Research Center.* Laurel, MD.

Shuford, W.D. 1993. *The Marin County Breeding Bird Atlas: A Distributional and Natural History of Coastal California Birds.* California Avifauna Series 1. Bushtit Books, Bolinas, California.

Shurtleff, L.L. and C. Savage. 1996. *The Wood Duck and the Mandarin.* Berkeley: University of California Press.

Skinner, M.P. 1938. "Western horned owl." pp.322-328. "Life histories of North American birds of prey, vol. 2." A.C. Bent, Ed. *U.S. Natl. Mus. Bull. 170.*

Sloane, S.A. 2001. "Bushtit." *The Birds of North America, No. 598.* A. Poole and F. Gill, Eds. The Birds of North America, Inc., Philadelphia, PA.

Sogge, M.K., W.M. Gilbert, and C.V. Riper III. 1994. "Orange-crowned Warbler." *The Birds of North America, No. 101.* A. Poole and F. Gill, Eds. The Academy of Natural Sciences, Philadelphia, PA, and The American Ornithologists' Union, Washington, D.C.

Spautz, H. 2002. "Tidal marsh song sparrow of San Francisco Bay, contaminants and nest success." *Observer No. 128,* p.3.

Steenhof, K. 1998. "Prairie Falcon." *The Birds of North America, No. 346.* A. Poole and F. Gill, Eds. The Birds of North America, Inc., Philadelphia, PA.

Storer, R.W. and G.L. Nuechterlein. 1992. "Western Grebe, Clark's Grebe." *The Birds of North America, No. 26.* A. Poole, P. Stettenheim, and F. Gill, Eds. The Academy of Natural Sciences, Philadelphia, PA, and The American Ornithologists' Union, Washington, D.C.

Trulio, L.A. 1995. "Passive relocation: a method to preserve burrowing owls on disturbed sites." *Journal of Field Ornithology 66:99-106.*

Turner, A. and C. Rose. 1989. *A handbook to the swallows and martins of the world.* London: Christopher Helm.

Twedt, D.J. and R.D. Crawford. 1995. "Yellow-headed Blackbird." *The Birds of North America, No. 192.* A. Poole and F. Gill, Eds. The Academy of Natural Sciences, Philadelphia, PA, and The American Ornithologists' Union, Washington, D.C.

Tyler, W.M. 1949. "Eastern Robin." pp.14-45. "Life histories of North American thrushes, kinglets, and their allies." A.C. Bent, Ed. *U.S. Natl. Mus. Bull. 196.*

Tyler, W.M. 1950. "Cedar Waxwing." pp.79-102. "Life histories of North American wagtails, shrikes, vireos, and their allies." *U.S. Natl. Mus. Bull. 197.*

REFERENCES

Vickery, P.D. 1996. "Grasshopper Sparrow." *The Birds of North America, No. 239.* A. Poole and F. Gill, Eds. The Academy of Natural Sciences, Philadelphia, PA, and The American Ornithologists' Union, Washington, D.C.

Walker, Lewis W. 1974. *The book of owls.* pp.129-151. New York: Alfred Knopf.

Watt, D.J. and E.J. Willoughby. 1999. "Lesser Goldfinch." *The Birds of North America, No. 392.* A. Poole and F. Gill, Eds. The Birds of North America, Inc., Philadelphia, PA.

Williams, L. 1958. "Brewer's Blackbird." pp.302-334. "Life histories of North American blackbirds, orioles, tanagers, and allies." A.C. Bent, Ed. *U.S. Natl. Mus. Bull. 211.*

Winkler, H., D.A. Christie, and D. Nurney. 1995. *Woodpeckers, a guide to the woodpeckers of the world.* Boston: Houghton Mifflin Co.

Witmer, M.C., D.J. Mountjoy, and L. Elliot. 1997. "Cedar Waxwing." *The Birds of North America, No. 309.* A. Poole and F. Gill, Eds. The Academy of Natural Sciences, Philadelphia, PA, and The American Ornithologists' Union, Washington, D.C.

Wolf, B.O. 1997. "Black Phoebe." *The Birds of North America, No. 268.* A. Poole and F. Gill, Eds. The Academy of Natural Sciences, Philadelphia, PA, and The American Ornithologists' Union, Washington, D.C.

Woods, R.S. 1968. "House finch." pp.290-314. "Life histories of North American cardinals, grosbeaks, buntings, towhees, finches, sparrows, and allies." O.L. Austin, Ed. *U.S. Natl. Mus. Bull. 237.*

Yasukawa, K. and W.A. Searcy. 1995. "Red-winged Blackbird." *The Birds of North America, No. 184.* A. Poole and F. Gill, Eds. The Academy of Natural Sciences, Philadelphia, PA, and The American Ornithologists' Union, Washington, D.C.

Yee, D.G., B.E. Deuel, and S.F. Bailey. 1990. "Middle Pacific Coast Region." *Am Birds 44:491-494.*

_____, B.E. Deuel, and S. F. Bailey. 1990. "Middle Pacific Coast Region." *Am Birds 44:1181-1184.*

Yee, D.G., S.F. Bailey, and B.E. Deuel. 1991. "The winter season, Middle Pacific Coast Region." *Am Birds 45:315-318.*

_____, S.F. Bailey, and B.E. Deuel. 1991. "Middle Pacific Coast Region." *Am Birds 45:491-494.*

_____, B.E., Deuel, and S.F. Bailey. 1991. "The summer season, Middle Pacific Coast Region." *Am Birds 45:1156-1160.*

Yee, D.G., S.F. Bailey, and B.E. Deuel. 1992. "The spring season, Middle Pacific Coast Region." *Am Birds 46:475-478.*

_____, S.F. Bailey, and B.E. Deuel. 1993. "Middle Pacific Coast Region." *Am Birds 47:1145-1148.*

INDEX

INDEX

(Foldout Map)

Napa County Vegetation